THE AUTODYNE

THE AUTODYNE
A NEW ELECTRICAL MACHINE

BY

PROF. OTTO BENEDIKT
TECHNICAL UNIVERSITY, BUDAPEST

SECOND REVISED EDITION

PERGAMON PRESS

OXFORD · LONDON · NEW YORK · PARIS

1960

PERGAMON PRESS LTD
Headington Hill Hall, Oxford
4 & 5 Fitzroy Square, London W. 1

PERGAMON PRESS INC.
122 East 55th Street, New York 22, N. Y.
P. O. Box 47715, Los Angeles, California

PERGAMON PRESS S.A.R.L.
24 Rue des Écoles, Paris Ve

PERGAMON PRESS, G.m.b.H.
Kaiserstrasse 75, Frankfurt-am-Main

First published in English 1960

Translated
by
G. TÉGLÁS

Supervised
by
F. CSÁKI
and
K. SZENDY

Library of Congress Card No. 59—15290

PRINTED IN HUNGARY

PREFACE

The invitation to contribute an introduction to this translation into English of Professor Benedikt's book "The Autodyne" gave me great pleasure. It was the occasion for renewing contact, at least by correspondence, with a colleague of more than 20 years ago, when I worked for a couple of years alongside Otto Benedikt in the design office of the Moscow Dynamo Works. In the Soviet Union at that time, through much effort and hardship, the first stages were being improvised of the development in engineering and technical education that today is so massive. Benedikt, a big man with irrepressible energy, was inventing then, and he is inventing still. He had many ideas about electrical machines, some of which seemed speculative, if not impracticable, against the background of scarcity and urgent immediate needs of that period. But it is noteworthy that he was provided with men and money to develop his machines, and I have often thought of "Benedikt's motors" as a signpost that could have indicated, to an imaginative eye, an assurance of a new world ahead.

Of what Professor Benedikt had done during the intervening period I know little, but now, as Professor of Electrical Engineering in the Technical High School of Budapest, he makes himself known to English-speaking engineers through his lucid account of a most ingenious new electrical machine — the Autodyne.

It is a pleasure also to introduce this book as adding one more to the number of translated works, through which the efforts of engineers in East and West are becoming available to each other. Our need for technical progress is a common need, and the time is coming, if it has not already come, when the scientific potential that has been built up in the Soviet Union and its associates will be a major and indispensable contribution to our common progress. It is greatly to be welcomed that, through the good services of the

Pergamon Press, this interesting and stimulating work will be made
more readily accessible.

    This novel machine, the Autodyne, is a very distinctive wen
member of the broad family of rotary amplifiers. It has the mark
of all true inventions — an essential simplicity. It springs from a
union of a firm grasp of the mode of operation of a rotary converter
with a lively appreciation of the possibilities of "feed-back" and gives
us, with a single machine, a means to obtain control of any quantity
that can be made to depend on a direct current, using the ordinary
fixed frequency a-c power supply as the source of energy. There is
no doubt that the basic idea is capable of many variants and of
further development.

    But this is not the place to discuss the technical aspects
and possibilities of the Autodyne. The book speaks very clearly for
itself, and it is certain to stimulate experiment and further development in the countries where English is read. Apart from the important technical possibilities of the invention it describes, the book
will give pleasure and instruction as a masterly exposition of the
logical application of fundamental principles.

Professor A. Tustin

M. Sc., M. I. E. E.
Department of Electrical Engineering,
Imperial College

AUTHOR'S PREFACE

Since the publication of the German edition, a vast correspondence, containing valuable hints as regards new fields of application for the Autodyne, as well as on the further analysis of theoretical problems and methods of their representation, has reached the author. Some of the readers suggested to devote more detailed attention to the previous works of other authors who had also attempted to develop controllable rotary converters, to reveal the reasons why these attempts failed to produce satisfactory results and, starting from this critical analysis, to describe in a more plastic manner the ways that have led to the development of the Autodynes. These suggestions have been accepted as fully justified and the edition of the book in English offered a suitable opportunity for complying with them. In order to meet these desires, the first three chapters have been rewritten and completed by the details mentioned.

Some readers apparently found the space devoted to problems of transient phenomena restricted, although, in their opinion, these problems are of paramount importance for control and amplifier type generators. There were again some who tentatively put forward that it would have been more correct to adopt for these phenomena, instead of the physical approach used, a more detailed mathematical one, as is common practice when dealing with modern automatics, of which the Autodyne represents a new element.

Questions of similar nature are likely to arise in the minds of the English readers as well. It seems therefore advisable to discuss these aspects in this place and to outline the considerations resulting in the maintenance of the original method of presentation for the English version also.

Though the Autodyne actually represents a new element of automatic regulation and control, it is, in the first place, a new electrical machine, and anyone intending to apply it in automatics must acquire familiarity with its operational characteristics. The fact, that this machine is in principle capaßle of replacing several machines by a single one in widely different fields of automatic regulation and control, can evidently not be exploited to advantage, unless it can be shown to be at least equivalent to those replaced, as far as its other operational properties are concerned. For this reason the problems to be dealt with in the first place are whether the principle underlying the operation of the Autodyne is suitable for ensuring reliable functioning; whether the control afforded is sufficiently accurate and extends over a sufficiently wide range; whether its static and dynamic commutation is sufficiently good; whether the power factor is satisfactory; whether its efficiency is high enough; whether or not the converter operation can be inverted; and finally whether the shape of the individual parts and the technology of their manufacture do not involve undue difficulties. Obviously, a sufficiently exhaustive investigation and convincing representation of the issues listed above, and of similar nature, is only possible if the treatment of transient phenomena is restricted accordingly. Under such circumstances, a physical-qualitative approach was necessarily preferred to a mathematical-quantitative one.

A further consideration, in addition to those listed above, was that, beyond its application for automatic regulation, the Autodyne is capable of replacing the motor-generator in a wide variety of other fields as well, where the transient phenomena play no significant role at all.

These considerations seem to justify the adherence to the subject matter and method of presentation of the German edition for the English version also, the primary purpose of which is to introduce a new electrical machine to readers who are as yet not familiar with the particular problems of the Autodyne. It is expected on the other hand to devote appreciably more space to transient phenomena of the Autodyne in a new edition of this book, when increased familiarity of a wider public with the new electrical machine can already be assumed.

The publication of the English edition offers a welcome opportunity to the author to express his indebtedness to Mr. G. TÉGLÁS, engineer, for the technical translation, to Mr. G. DIENES, editor, for his linguistic help and editing work, to Mr. K. SZENDY, doctor of technical sciences, who reviewed the manuscript, and to my immediate collaborator Professor F. CsÁKI, candidate of technical sciences, for his valuable expert suggestions.

Sincere appreciation is, at the same time, expressed to the Pergamon Press and the Publishing House of the Hungarian Academy of Sciences for the publication of this book in English, as well as to the employees of the Academy Press for their careful work.

The Author

AUTHOR'S PREFACE TO THE GERMAN EDITION

During the long years of scientific work I spent in the Soviet Union, thanks to the hospitality of the Soviet Government, I had the opportunity to meet personally Mr. K. SCHENFER, member of the Academy of Sciences of the USSR, and to become acquainted with the new ideas expounded in the wide field of activity of this versatile scientist. One of SCHENFER's works, in which I was particularly interested, referred to his experiments in controlling the d-c voltage of a rotary converter independently of the a-c voltage, the former being known to be proportional to the latter.

Although SCHENFER has, in the last analysis, not succeeded in constructing a machine free of the main disadvantages of rotary converters — which, in fact, impeded the practical realization of his proposals — his work showed possibilities (and this is his great merit) of improving significantly the operational properties of the rotary converter.

Being convinced that a motor generator can be substituted by a converter with adjustable d-c voltage (that is, by a single machine of smaller dimensions and higher efficiency, which is very likely to have for many purposes a very great importance) I began to work on this problem in 1941, whereby I analysed theoretically all circumstances that had made such a transformation difficult until then.

This analysis has led to the conclusion that a truly successful solution of the above problem could only become possible by renouncing what had till then been held a fundamental condition of the operation principle of rotary converters — namely to produce an exciting field along a definite axis. Its substitution by a *"rotor slip excitation"* enabled me to make the d-c voltage totally independent of the a-c voltage. Herewith another very important result was achieved, the possibility of producing big variations by small power impulses of the d-c voltage and of the power produced by it, that is to say to use the machine as an amplifier. Owing to this, the converter could be used not only as a power converter replacing a motor generator by a single machine but also instead of a motor-driven amplidyne used for automatic stabilization or control of definite quantities.

Tests on converters proved the correctness of the basic idea underlying the invention and showed the possibility of realizing it with the most different schemes, whereby the new machine, which I called *"autodyne"*, displayed, according to its scheme, the most different characteristics and properties.

In the experimental stage, emphasis was laid, first of all, upon the clarification of the theoretical problems of principle, such as the possibility of control and automatic performance, while questions of commutation, power factor or economy were at that time considered less important.

Nevertheless, when the positive results of the tests made it clear that the new machine was able to be applied within a wide range, the afore-mentioned questions considered of less importance came to the foreground and claimed solution.

Theoretical investigations showed the possibility of substituting the "rotor slip excitation" by the principle of the *"stator slip excitation"* which, in turn, resulted in a complete solution of commutating problems in steady-state condition, in eliminating the reactive magnetizing current taken up by the rotor and causing the lowering of the efficiency and power factor. Thus, the basis was created for investing the new machine with an interesting property, by utilizing the phenomenon which I called *"rotor overexcitation"*. This consists of feeding relatively great amounts of reactive power into the supplying network with simultaneous conversion of power, without the necessity to convey any additional heat or to ensure additional space, as is necessary in case of *"stator overexcitation"* of a converter.

Since the autodyne — either as a power converter or a control-type machine — is applicable also in fields where the load varies instantaneously, and thus a rotary converter undergoes oscillations and shows commutation difficulties, it was necessary to treat theoretically the transient phenomena occurring under these circumstances in the converter, as well as to solve the problem of their

elimination in case they should occur in the autodyne. These investigations have shown that no such phenomena are likely to occur in
the autodyne but if they still do, they can readily be compensated
for by the *"forcing winding"*.

When all important basic problems of the autodyne for
practical application were thus solved theoretically, the Moscow
Institute of Transport Engineers (MITE)* where at that time I held
a chair, decided to build an autodyne in order to check the invention
experimentally. A test work of long years with the machine showed
a complete conformity of practical results with those that were
to be expected on the basis of the theory. The machine worked satis-
factorily and steadily under instantaneous load variations also, it
stabilized and controlled definite quantities in widely varying
schemes and on the basis of widely varying laws. It proved possible
in practice to start d-c motors without starting resistances and to
control their speed continuously within a wide range, to charge and
to form accumulator batteries, to control other machines, and so on.

The positive results induced the Ministry of Electrical
Industry of the USSR to have a new series of experimental autodynes
(Type AB) built under the supervision of the author in the experimental factory of its Research Institute. As these machines also
proved completely satisfactory, the large-scale production of autodynes (Type AZ) was started, to replace the AZD type motor generators
destined for charging accumulator batteries. Both in successful labo-
ratory tests and in operation these autodynes also were found reliable
under such conditions as charging batteries automatically with constant current and discharging (forming) with energy recuperation
to the a-c mains through the autodyne. At the same time it has
become evident that the use of the autodyne saves energy and the
price of the machine is soon recovered.

Autodynes have successfully been used for a number of years
for charging railway carriage batteries. It is to be expected that a
large number of serially produced autodynes, type AZ—140/72, will
be in service in the nearest future over the network of the USSR
Ministry of Transport.

As a result of many years work of Soviet engineers, a new
machine was designed, a machine likely to be applicable in many an

* In Russian : МИИТ (Московский Институт Инженеров Транспорта)

important field of engineering and to enlarge considerably the possibilities of automatic electrical control. It is expected to be useful not only in the field of accumulators, but also in electric welding, in supplying d-c motor drives, for control, amplification purposes etc.

In connection with my appointment to the Technical University, Budapest, I considered it my duty to accept the honourable proposal of the Hungarian Academy of Sciences to write a book on the theory of the autodyne. It is quite natural that the limits placed at my disposal permitted the treating only of the most important basic problems and that too in a simplified form, without dealing in detail with computation methods and design particularities. This treatment must be left to a later work.

The references in this book to the experimental verification of built autodynes, to their different types, main dimensions, weights and other tabulated data, as well as to the economical computations of the autodyne type AZ—140/72, relate to the investigation of Docent and Candidate of engineering sciences A. E. ZOROKHOVICH, who was for long years my collaborator and who carried out part of the relevant works by himself, analysing them systematically, for which I thank him cordially now. And I avail myself of the opportunity to thank D. EFREMOV, former Minister of Electrical Industry and N. BORISHENKO, Deputy Minister of Electrical Industry for their organizing help, as well as my collaborators, Candidates of engineering sciences, V. RATMIROV, T. AMBARZUMOV and S. BARSKY and engineers L. SHALMAN and E. KOVARSKY for the scientific support by which they contributed to the realization of the new machine.

In connection with the publication of my book by the Hungarian Academy of Sciences I am indebted to Docent and Candidate of engineering sciences, F. CSÁKI, the scientific supervisor of the manuscript, for his thorough criticism and extremely valuable and useful hints. My thanks are due to the Publishing House of the Hungarian Academy of Sciences and to the workers of the Szeged printing office for the careful setting and printing of the book.

I hope this book will contribute to the scientific popularization and economic application beyond the Soviet Union of this new electrical machine developed in a work of long years in the USSR, and will promote a closer contact between nations by the interchange of their cultural achievements.

The Author

CONTENTS

REPLACING A MOTOR GENERATOR SET
BY A ROTARY CONVERTER

In engineering, motor generator sets capable of varying their d-c voltage within broad limits are widely used for producing d-c power, though they have great disadvantages, e.g., large dimensions, ponderous weight, considerable power losses, and also the necessity of transmitting the mechanical power through a shaft. When an asynchronous machine is used as a driving motor, further drawbacks are added, such as the low power factor, especially at partial load, and, in case of sudden changes in load, the considerable and eventually abrupt decrease of the speed.

It is a well-known fact that rotary converters are free from these disadvantages. They have only one common field-magnet system and convert a-c power into d-c power directly in one armature winding, connected electrically to a commutator. Hereby, in this winding the current of the a-c system is opposite to that of the d-c system, which results in a substantial decrease of weight, dimensions and power losses. The converter can work with a unity power factor or even with a leading one. Finally, the power is not transmitted through any shaft.

Rotary converters could have even greater advantages, if they could replace machine groups comprising a number of d-c generator sets driven by a d-c motor mounted on a common shaft. In such cases, as for instance in excavators, the dimensions of the whole mechanism are considerably enlarged because of the great length of the machine set. Should it be possible to substitue for the latter a number of converters mounted in different places, the space requirements and the weight of the whole mechanism could be substantially diminished.

In spite of the advantages described, the converter could not, for a long time, be used as a substitute for motor generator sets,

because the d-c voltage cannot be controlled by an ordinary converter within a wide range.

In these machines the magnetic flux induces d-c voltage or
electromotive force (emf) between brushes A and B in the d-c winding 1
(Fig. 1) and a-c voltage or emf in the three phases $a-b$, $b-c$, $c-a$
of the same winding. The former is induced by the entire flux Φ',
whilst the latter by the spatial fundamental Φ'_1 of flux Φ'. If the number of effective turns of the phase wind-
ings on the rotor is $N_{R\sim}$ and the effective number of turns of the series-
connected rotor windings between
brushes A and B is $N_{R=}$, then the
ratio of the d-c voltage generated between the brushes to the effective value
of voltage induced in the phase windings, will be proportional to the ratio

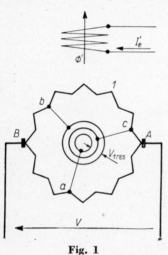

Fig. 1

$$\frac{\Phi' \, N_{R=}}{\Phi'_1 \, N_{R\sim}}$$

The ratio Φ'/Φ'_1 being, at a given
configuration of the magnetic circuit,
practically independent of the operating conditions, it follows that the ratio
of internal voltages or emfs will also be constant.

Neglecting all losses, the voltage induced in the phase windings at no load is equal to the mains voltage V_{1res}, and the voltage
induced between the brushes equals the external d-c voltage V.
Consequently, the use of conventional rotary converters as a source
of controlled d-c voltage is out of question.

Yet at first glance the voltage V appears to be controllable
by changing the exciting current I'_e. However, as revealed by the theory
of rotary converters, this is not actually the case, inasmuch as by,
e.g., increasing the current I'_e and thereby inducing a change in the
voltage (or emf) within the phase windings, the three-phase network
will act with respect to these latter as a closed circuit, since the mains
voltage V_{1res} is balanced by the existing voltage (or emf) in the phase
windings. Under the influence of the additional voltage (or emf),
a three-phase current is created in the rotor winding, the mmf of
which practically compensates the additional stator mmf due to the

increase of I'_e. This current, playing an important role in the theory of conventional rotary converters, and being also of outstanding significance for explaining the processes taking place in the autodyne, will hereafter be referred to as "compensation current". It prevents the departure of the voltage (or emf), induced in the phase windings, from the value which it should assume to balance the mains voltage V_{1res}. It is to be seen, therefore, that the impossibility of controlling the internal voltages (or emfs) and therewith the d-c voltage V in the machine represented in *Fig. 1,* has indeed well-founded physical reasons.

The situation remains unaltered even if the ratio $N_{R=}/N_{R\sim}$ is modified which, as is well-known, can in principle be accomplished by connecting additional phase windings between the points a, b, c on the one hand, and, the appurtenant slip rings on the other, or by replacing the common d-c and a-c winding by two completely separated windings. True enough, by selecting an appropriate number of turns, other values of V can be attained at the previous mains voltage V_{1res}, yet rotary converters built according to one of the above solutions have again an uncontrollable fixed voltage V, although of different magnitude.

Conventional rotary converters are unsuited for application not only in fields requiring the regulation of the voltage V, but also where constant voltage is required. This is due to the fact that the simplified conditions assumed previously, and involving the constancy of the ratio V/V_{1res}, do not actually prevail. Owing especially to the occurrence of voltage losses when loading, the induced phase voltage (or emf) varies relative to V_{1res}, and V varies relative to the induced d-c voltage (or emf). Yet even at no load the constancy of V can hardly be relied upon, since the mains voltage V_{1res} itself is subject to frequent fluctuations and every change is reflected in the magnitude of V.

All of the more significant attempts hitherto reported for controlling, at least within certain limits, conventional rotary converters have used methods relying on essentially different principles.

In one of these experiments it was sought to control the magnitude of the voltage V_{1res} acting on the phase windings, which, in keeping with the considerations outlined above, necessarily entails the proportionate variation of V. A transformer, or auto-transformer with taps can, e.g., be inserted between the network and

2*

the slip rings. Under load a choke coil may also be applied instead of the former, and the magnitude of the voltage drop can be controlled by changing the inductivity of the coil, or else by creating a compensating current through the increase or reduction of current I_e'. This compensating current represents capacitive or inductive no-load current, which induces in the choke coil a voltage drop of a direction increasing or reducing $V_{1\text{res}}$. The main common disadvantage of all these methods is, however, that the reduction of $V_{1\text{res}}$, without which evidently no wide-range control can be attained, is possible only between relatively narrow limits. The reason for this is that the synchronizing torque of rotary converters diminishes as the square of the supply voltage, and the danger of falling out of phase, rapidly arises. It is obvious furthermore that the rating of the necessary additional machines attains practically impermissible magnitudes, as the control range is widened.

The other method of controlling V, though based on the given voltage $V_{1\text{res}}$, attempts to modify the ratio Φ'/Φ_1' by applying auxiliary windings to change the distribution of induction and also, in turn, the share of the spatial upper harmonics thereof. Yet the results that can be expected by this method are evidently very moderate, in view of the appreciably more involved constructional arrangement it requires.

None of the methods outlined above can be applied to replace a motor generator set by a rotary converter, the main characteristic of the former being that the d-c voltage V created by them can be varied continuously from a positive value $+V_{\max}$ through zero to a negative value $-V_{\max}$.

Consequently, we are interested only in such suggestions of controlling the d-c voltage of rotary converters, that endeavour to enlarge the narrow control range of conventional rotary converters and to transform the latter into a machine, which, while preserving the considerable advantages of conventional rotary converters, such as compactness, high efficiency, possibility of creating a capacitive no-load current, etc., provide simultaneously for a wide-range control and a continuous reversal of the d-c voltage V. Similar attempts at the solution of the problem were based on two fundamentally different principles. These attempts, namely the machines of SCHENFER and MELLER, though they failed to find a definite solution and are no longer remembered, should be regarded as very interesting.

EARLIER ATTEMPTS AT SOLVING
THE PROBLEM

In 1928, K. SCHENFER, ordinary member of the Academy of Sciences of the USSR, proposed the following original method of controlling the d-c voltage of the converter within a wide range. According to his proposal, the stator of the machine has two exciting windings acting along two axes perpendicular to each other. By varying the magnetomotive forces (mmfs) in both windings, the spatial position of the field, consisting of a direct-axis and a quadrature-axis component, can be varied. The resulting field remains at the same time practically constant in every position, because the phase voltage generated by it has to be in equilibrium with the given mains voltage. It follows herefrom that, by increasing the flux along the quadrature axis, the direct-axis component and with it the d-c voltage generated between the fixed brushes are bound to decrease. By the use of the control principle proposed by K. SCHENFER, it became thus possible to obtain a continuously variable voltage within the limits $+V_{max}$ and $-V_{max}$ between the brushes of the converter.

It is not difficult to understand that the scheme, called hereafter *"general scheme of rotary converters"*, represents the general case for this type of machines, referred to hereafter as *"generalized rotary converters"*, while the *"ordinary"* rotary converter shown in *Fig. 1* is a particular case, in which the quadrature component of the flux is absent.

In order to illustrate the applicability of the principle outlined above to the continuous control of the d-c voltage of a rotary converter, an example will be given to explain certain fundamental considerations frequently referred to later.

One of the two above-mentioned excitation windings should be assumed to act along the direct axis of the machine, the other along the quadrature axis *(Fig. 2a)*.

For the sake of simplicity, the permeance of the machine will be assumed to be identical in all directions, the machine to operate at no load, and the copper and iron losses to be negligible.

In addition to this, all internal torques as, for instance, the frictional torque, will be neglected. *Fig. 2a* shows the circuit diagram of such a machine, on which the slip rings feeding the armature with a three-phase current, are not shown. The exciting current I'_e produces a vertical mmf F'_e* acting along the so-called direct axis, while the

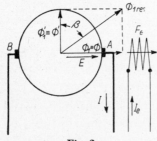

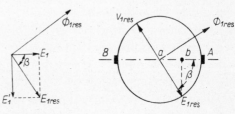

| Fig. 2a | Fig. 2b | Fig. 2c |

exciting current I_e creates a horizontal mmf F_e, acting along the so-called quadrature axis. These mmfs together establish a flux, whose spatial fundamental Φ_{1res} forms the angle β with the direct axis of the machine. This flux induces in the armature the emf E_{1res} leading by a 90° time angle *(Fig. 2b).***

Resolve now, the flux Φ_{1res} into a component,

$$\Phi'_1 = \Phi_{1res} \cos \beta \tag{1}$$

acting along the direct axis of the machine and into a component,

$$\Phi_1 = \Phi_{1res} \sin \beta \tag{2}$$

acting along the quadrature axis. Here Φ'_1 represents the spatial fundamental of the actual direct-axis flux Φ', and Φ_1 is the spatial fundamental of the actual quadrature-axis flux Φ.

---

* Here as hereafter, where stator mmfs are mentioned in principle, i.e. without referring to an actual arrangement as to poles, the quantity F refers to the mmf per pole.

** The armature rotates clockwise. The vectors are stationary in space, i.e. can be said to rotate counterclockwise, if related to the rotation of the armature.

The total flux Φ' generates the d-c emf between the brushes A and B. Consequently, by taking into account the constant speed of the armature, we obtain

$$E \equiv \Phi'^*$$

Since the quantities Φ/Φ_1 and Φ'/Φ_1' in fact depend on the configuration of the machine alone, and are therefore constant, and since Φ_{1res} and E_{1res} are proportional to each other, we have

$$E = c_1 E_{1res} \cos \beta \tag{3}**$$

c_1 being a factor of proportionality. If $\beta = 0$

$$E_0 = E_{max} = c_1 E_{1res} \tag{4}$$

It follows that

$$E = E_{max} \cos \beta \tag{5}$$

By resolving the emf vector $\overline{E_{1res}}$, in the diagram of the time vectors *(Fig. 2b)* referring to one phase, into the components

$$E_1 = E_{1res} \cos \beta \tag{6}$$

and

$$E_1' = E_{1res} \sin \beta \tag{7}$$

we obtain from (3) and (6)

$$E = c_1 E_1 \tag{8}$$

It results from this that the angle between the direction of the quadrature axis of brushes B and A, along which E is acting *(Fig. 2a)*, and the spatial direction of $\overline{\Phi_{1res}}$ has the same value, $90° - \beta$, as the angle between the time vectors $\overline{E_1}$ and $\overline{\Phi_{1res}}$.

Hence, by plotting the diagram of phase vectors *(Fig. 2b)* in a position in which vector $\overline{\Phi_{1res}}$ parallels vector $\overline{\Phi_{1res}}$ in *Fig. 2a*, the direction of emf E in *Fig. 2a* is found to coincide with the direction of vector component $\overline{E_1}$ in *Fig. 2b*.

Very instructive illustrations can be obtained by superposing *Fig. 2a*, representing space relations, and *Fig. 2b*, representing time relations, as shown in *Fig. 2c*. The vector $\overline{\Phi_{1res}}$ of the spatial funda-

---

* Here and hereafter the sign $\equiv$ will be used for denoting proportionality.
** For Eq. (3a) see p. 28.

mental of the flux is used at the same time as time vector $\overline{\Phi}_{1res}$ inducing emf $\overline{E}_{1res}$ in the phase winding. By this method the emf vector $\overline{E}_{1res}$ and the axis of the brushes B and A form the angle β. Thus a readily apprehensible representation of the influence of the spatial position of vector $\overline{\Phi}_{1res}$ on quantity E is achieved, because $\overline{E}_{1res}$ is perpendicular to vector $\overline{\Phi}_{1res}$, while quantity E is proportional to the projection $a - b$ of vector $\overline{E}_{1res}$ on the quadrature axis of brushes B and A.

According to the method used, all other phase vectors have to be brought into compliance with the general vector diagram whereby their position is determined by the relative position compared to time vectors $\overline{\Phi}_{1res}$ and $\overline{E}_{1res}$. E.g. vector $\overline{V}_{1res}$ of the mains phase voltage which, according to our simplifying assumption, equalizes the emf vector $\overline{E}_{1res}$, assumes a position opposite to vector $\overline{E}_{1res}$, whence the magnitudes of the vectors mentioned equal each other.*

As convincingly demonstrated by *Fig. 2c*, the arrangement according to *Fig. 2a*, is actually suitable for continuously regulating the d-c voltage of a rotary converter within a wide range. The limits of this range are also shown in *Fig. 2c*. If the mutual ratio of the currents I'_e and I_e is varied so as to make the fluxes Φ'_1 and Φ' satisfy simultaneously both equations (1) and (2), the vector Φ_{1res} will rotate correspondingly in space according to *Fig. 2c*, together with the vectors $\overline{E}_{1res}$ and $\overline{V}_{1res}$, while the d-c voltage will be proportional to the distance $a - b$. As point b can assume any possible position along the diameter connecting the two brushes A and B, it is obvious that the d-c voltage E can be regulated continuously from the value $+E_{max}$ (at $\beta = 0°$) over zero (at $\beta = 90°$) to $-E_{max}$ (at $\beta = 180°$).

Neither do these results suffer essential changes, if the hitherto neglected frictional torque T_f is taken into account in the vector diagram *(Fig. 3)*.

* For the sake of simplicity it is assumed that, after having superposed *Figs. 2a* and *2b*, the positive directions of the vectors Φ_1 and E_1 are the same in *Fig. 2c* as before. Hence $+ \Phi_1$ (and similarly the flux Φ too) is directed from left to right, while $+ E_1$ (and therefore the voltage E too) acts in the same direction. On the other hand, the positive directions of Φ'_1 and E'_1 are opposite.

When frictional torque is present, the armature cannot revolve synchronously, unless the said torque is in equilibrium with the electrodynamic torque T due to Φ_{1res} and the armature current. The function of the latter is accomplished by the motor phase current I_f (*Fig. 3*). The flux produced by it induces a voltage E_f, in consequence of which an angle γ forms between vectors $+\overline{E_{1res}}$ and $-\overline{V_{1res}}$.

It follows that the role of the total voltage induced both by flux $\overline{\Phi_{1res}}$ due to the stator mmfs F'_e and F_e and by the flux due to the armature mmf produced by the current I_f, is adopted by the emf $\overline{E_{1res}} + \overline{E_f}$, balanced by voltage V_{1res}. Thus while in case of *Fig. 2c* the emf E is proportional to the projection of emf $\overline{E_{1res}}$ on the axis $B - A$, here E is proportional to the projection of vector $\overline{E_{1res}} + \overline{E_f}$ on this axis. This means that by neglecting the voltage drop, the voltage between brushes A and B is

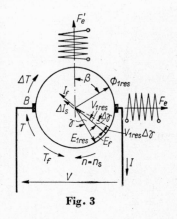

Fig. 3

$$V = c_1 V_{1res} \cos (\beta - \gamma) \tag{9}$$

The occurrence of angle γ can be seen to cause no significant changes in the results obtained previously, since as long as $\beta = 0°$, i.e. in the case of conventional rotary converters, V remains constant for any given V_{1res}. On the other hand, if the angle β is varied continuously over the range from $\beta = \gamma$ to $\beta = 180 + \gamma$ by correspondingly modifying the mmfs F_e and F'_e, the value V will also vary continuously between the values $\pm V_{max}$.

Beside the fundamental types shown in *Fig. 2*, K. SCHENFER proposed quite a number of modifications of the general scheme, especially for welding machines. He added to one of the exciting windings mentioned above a series winding, acting along the same axis, or — as another alternative — replaced the winding in question by the latter, in order to obtain a strongly decreasing voltage with increasing current.

It is proposed now to describe the fundamentally different approach followed by MELLER in 1926 in two papers.* His

* *(E. und M.* 1926, no. 9 and no. 37.)

basic concept will be discussed hereafter, using the method outlined above.

Let us assume the excitation winding of the stator in *Fig. 1*
to be removed. The rotor 4, fed over the slip rings 1, 2, 3 of the rotary
converter RC *(Fig. 4)*, acts in this case as a three-phase choke coil
and the flux $\overline{\Phi_{1res}}$, which induces the emf $\overline{E_{1res}}$ compensating the

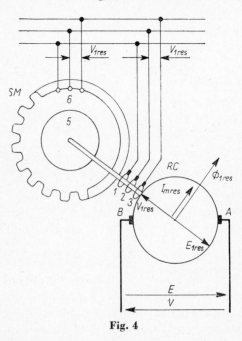

mains voltage $\overline{V_{1res}}$, will be
excited by a magnetizing
rotor current $\overline{I_{mres}}$ supplied
by the network. If the rotor
revolves — in a manner
similar to that in *Figs. 1*
and *2* — synchronously, the
flux will be stationary in
space, as a result of which
the d-c emf arising between
the brushes *A* and *B* will
remain constant as well (see
also *Fig. 2c*). Adopting further the same simplifying
assumptions as in connection
with *Fig. 2*, it will be found
that the flux Φ_{1res} can
assume any arbitrary direction in space, indicating —
as demonstrated previously

Fig. 4

— that the d-c emf is free to vary between the limits $\pm E_{max}$.
Now there arises the question of what forces the rotor to run at
synchronous speed, and prevents it from accelerating or decelerating. In the machine connected according to *Fig. 2*, this is the resultant
stator mmf, which forces the flux Φ_{1res} to assume and to maintain
the same direction. This orienting force, however, is missing in the
case of the machine RC shown in *Fig. 4*.

MELLER attempted to solve this problem by the application
of a separate synchronous machine SM coupled mechanically to the RC.

By making the same simplifying assumptions for the synchronous machine as for the machine RC, it becomes obvious that
the mmf $\overline{F_R}$, due to the rotor current *(Fig. 5)*, is lagging behind the

voltage with a phase shift of 90°, while the mmf $\overline{F}_S$, due to the
stator current, leads by 90°. Their difference $\overline{F}_\phi$ creates the main
flux inducing the internal voltage (emf), which balances the main
voltage V_{1res}. Any deceleration or acceleration of the two coupled
rotors 4 and 5 would create a torque in the SM,
which would tend to synchronize the two arma-
tures again.

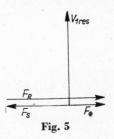

Fig. 5

 The problem for MELLER to solved
remained now under these circumstances to attain
the displacement of the flux Φ_{1res}, which had
been recognised as a prerequisite for the variation of the d-c voltage. His answer to the problem was to mount the stator of the synchronous
machine in a manner permitting its rotation, as shown schematically
in *Fig. 4*, e.g. by means of toothed gears 7. The vectors $\overline{V}_{1res}$, $\overline{F}_S$
and $\overline{F}_\phi$ in *Fig. 5* rotate together with the stator, if the latter is
turned, and the armature is forced thereby to revolve as long as
the vector $\overline{F}_R$ coincides with the new direction of $\overline{F}_\phi$. MELLER in this
way attained the same effect by mechanical means as SCHENFER did
by electrical ones.

 A further possibility for the continuous regulation of the
d-c voltage was also pointed out by MELLER in his paper mentioned
before. In order to understand the scheme proposed by him, let us
first present the problem in a general manner.

 Consider the machine RC illustrated in *Fig. 4*, disconnected
from the synchronous machine SM. Nevertheless, the rotor of the
former will continue to revolve synchronously, since all internal
torques, as, e.g. the one caused by friction,
have been assumed negligible. Yet the
situation will be fundamentally different
if the frictional torque T_f is also considered. Being opposed to the sense of rotation, the latter will exert a braking effect
and will tend to turn the flux Φ_{1res} in an
anticlockwise direction. This displacement can, however, be prevented by
providing mmf IN directed to the right
in the quadrature axis *(Fig. 6)*, which,

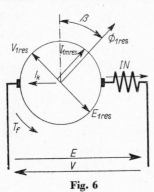

Fig. 6

together with the direct-axis component Φ_1 of the flux $\Phi_{1\text{res}}$, produces a torque obviously proportional to the product $\Phi_1' IN$ and with
a sense opposing that of T_f. Equilibrium will be established if the two
torques are equal. Hence it follows that in this case Φ_1' must be
proportionate to T_f/IN. Thus, considering Eqs. (3) and (1), we
obtain

$$E = c_1 E_{1\text{res}} \cos \beta = c_1 E_{1\text{res}} \frac{\Phi_1'}{\Phi_{1\text{res}}} = \frac{c_1 E_{1\text{res}} T_f}{c \Phi_{1\text{res}} IN} \tag{3a}$$

where $c = $ constant. It will be seen from this that emf E can be
regulated continuously in this manner by varying the current I.
MELLER applied, as shown in *Fig. 6*, the load current so as to give
the volt—ampère characteristic a hyperbolical shape.

Let us now make a critical approach to the proposals of
SCHENFER and MELLER. Owing to their inherent disadvantages, neither
of these has met with any practical success. A careful analysis of the
under lying reasons may reveal all the difficulties encountered and
indicate the way in which the replacement of the motor generator
set by a rotary converter can be attempted successfully.

Consider first the disadvantages of the arrangement in
Fig. 4. The main feature to be mentioned here is that, although friction appears at the first glance as the only resistance to be overcome
by the driving synchronous machine, the latter must actually be
designed with appreciably larger dimensions. It should be remembered that for maintaining stability the rotary converters, like all
synchronous machines, necessitate sufficiently high synchronizing
torques, which tend to re-establish synchronism, should this be disturbed. In the machines *Figs. 1* and *2*, these torques arise under
the combined effect of the mmfs in the stator and of the currents
in the armature. However, in the case illustrated in *Fig. 4*,
no synchronizing torques arise in the rotary converter if synchronism
is disturbed, since the stator windings are missing. Stability can thus
be maintained by the synchronizing torques in the machine SM only.
These, in turn, can be assumed as proportionate to the apparent power
of the machine. The necessity of considerably overdimensioning the
machine SM follows from this. Yet it will be perceived that the latter
cannot attain the degree of stability of a rotary converter, inasmuch
as, in addition to the inertia of its own armature, that of the armature
of the RC machine must also be overcome. The main advantage of

rotary converters over motor generator sets, namely that of consisting of a single machine, is thus lost.

It will further be readily appreciated that considerable difficulties in commutation are bound to arise in the machine RC, since the quadrature-axis flux Φ_1 obviously intersects in part the zone of commutation.

The magnetizing current supplied by the network results, on the one hand, in a diminution of efficiency, and, on the other, in a reduction of the permissible load current with due regard to thermal conditions. These circumstances constitute a further appreciable disadvantage of the arrangement according to *Fig. 4.*

The fact, finally, that the stator of the machine SM must be rotated mechanically, should also be considered an extraordinarily great disadvantage of this arrangement, since obviously the possibility of regulating similar machines with small power, and having a response time common to motor generator sets is naturally excluded. What is more, if it were, in principle, permissible to adopt a similar method of mechanical control, it would appear even simpler in the conventional rotary converter, according to *Fig. 1,* to rotate the brush ring and thereby to regulate the voltage V. However, notwithstanding mechanical difficulties, such measures were bound to fail on account of commutation problems, since the brushes would leave the neutral zone and be influenced by the main field.

Let us now subject MELLER's second proposal *(Fig. 6)* to a more rigorous investigation.

Synchronizing effect is not sufficiently guaranteed by this arrangement either. Although there is a stator mmf, this is incomparably smaller than the exciting mmfs in *Figs. 1* or *2,* because of being dimensioned, unlike the latter, for the frictional power only and not for the whole transmitted power.

The arrangement shown in *Fig. 6* has considerable disadvantages not only in dynamical respects but also in its operational characteristics. As revealed by Eq. (3a), the coherence between the emf E and the load current I is fixed for a given frictional torque, i.e. the machine has a single volt—ampère characteristic only, while voltage can be regulated continuously at a given load current by the aid of a motor generator set. It should be considered further that the frictional torque is far from constant in magnitude, but is subject to appreciable fluctuations, so that not even the afore-mentioned single characteristic actually represents a well-defined curve, but a rather broad band.

It will be noted further from Eq. (3a) that, in order to diminish the emf E to zero, the current I should be increased to ∞, i.e. the d-c voltage can neither be reversed nor be reduced to zero. It follows finally from the same equation that it only retains its validity down to a certain minimum value of the current I, that is, MELLER's machine drops out of phase at no load.

As revealed by the above considerations, the arrangement according to *Fig. 6* is incapable of competing with the motor generator set, on account of its operational characteristics alone.

The foregoing investigations point to the conclusion that, of the three arrangements described above designed with the aim of solving the problem of continuous voltage regulation, the one in *Fig. 2* appears to be the best. This arrangement requires no auxiliary motor, the exciting mmf in the stator is of the same order of magnitude as in a conventional rotary converter *(Fig. 1)*, consequently the synchronizing torques are similar in magnitude, and finally no magnetizing current passes through the armature.

Nevertheless, the arrangement shown in *Fig. 2* found no practical application and could not assert itself against the motor generator set. This appears to be due to the following three main reasons:

1. The d-c emf E obtained at a given angle β between the brushes is not constant, even at no load, but — in keeping with Eq. (3) — proportionate to the mains voltage $V_{1\mathrm{res}}$, known to be subject sometimes to appreciable fluctuations.

2. The well-known objectionable feature of rotary converters *(Fig. 1)* is that, in case of sudden load surges, the change of the alternating current in the armature lags behind the change of the direct current, which gives rise to a quadrature-axis mmf in the armature, while the latter, together with the stator flux acting in the direct axis, produces a torque. Oscillations of the rotor are thereby started, and the normal equilibrium between the armature mmfs, due to the direct and alternating currents, are disturbed. The consequence of this is the creation of quadrature-axis mmfs periodically changing their direction. This causes great difficulties in "dynamical" commutation. Since in the arrangement in *Fig. 2*, there is also a direct-

axis flux Φ', changes in load in it will be accompanied by similar phenomena.

Considering that motor generators are in many instances applied under conditions where great changes in load are frequent, which the generator can easily cope with, it will become evident that even arrangements, corresponding in principle to the one shown in *Fig. 2*, cannot compete successfully with them.

3. The last decades witnessed a rapid development aiming at ensuring automatically a special shape for the external characteristics of d-c generators. This was achieved either by the application of special windings or circuits (e.g. the machines of KRÄMER, or ROSENBERG), or else by building the generator as a rotary amplifier (e.g. the Amplydine). Obviously, the arrangement in *Fig. 2* was unable to meet these up-to-date requirements.

However, a successful attempt to construct a rotary converter, not only free from the disadvantages mentioned above, but also suitable for application as a control type machine, or even as a rotary amplifier, would be of utmost significance, because the more the machine capacity is increased. the more the fundamental objections against motor generators become the more apparent.

Difficulties often arise from the fact that control-type machines need a drive or have to be mounted on the shaft of the controlled machine, which requires the shaft of the machine group to be lengthened.

With sudden changes in load, the speed of the asynchronous motor driving the control type generator may decrease considerably, and even its stability may be affected. In addition to this, a further increase in the capacity of many electrical control type machines will cause difficulties calling for theoretical solution.

Relying on the critical analysis of the relevant attempts described hitherto, we have set ourselves the task of eliminating all the above disadvantages and shortcomings of rotary converters. As a result of long years of theoretical and experimental work on this problem, started and performed by the author as a leader of various groups of scientific collaborators, thanks to the hospitality of the Soviet Union, a new machine — the *AUTODYNE* — has been developed. *The autodyne has none of the above-mentioned disadvantages of rotary converters but has, unlike motor generator sets, all the advantages with regard to space requirements, weight, efficiency and the possibility*

*of feeding leading current into the mains. In addition, it has the following
qualities :*

*1. The autodyne is the combination of an energy converter and
of a control-type machine based on new principles, acting automatically.*

*2. The autodyne is able to control automatically any electrical
quantity either constant or varying, according to definite laws.*

*3. Most types of autodynes can be controlled by a much smaller
power than the exciting power of ordinary generators. For this reason,
the autodyne is also a new type of electrical amplifier.*

CHAPTER 3

ESTABLISHING INDIFFERENT EQUILIBRIUM OF THE MAGNETIC SYSTEM IN A D-C GENERATOR

In order to find the way permitting the step-by-step transformation of the rotary converter into a machine capable of automatic control and amplification, it is proposed to apply the following method:

Since all conventional types of rotary amplifiers repre sent, without exception, d-c generators, let us select one of them which, on the one hand, can be developed by relatively simple means from a conventional d-c generator and, on the other, requires very little power for control purposes. A similar machine is, e.g., the well-known "Regulex". This, as is commonly known, is essentially a shunt generator *(Fig. 7c)*. In its field circuit "critical resistance" prevails. This machine, like all amplifiers, can be operated in widely different connections, depending upon the automatic characteristics required, e.g. in one connection its own load current can be maintained constant regardless of the load resistance, or, what amounts to the same, voltage is regulated in proportion to the latter *(Fig. 7b)*. This connection had been familiar — as the so-called three-winding machine of KRÄMER — long before it was realized that it was just one of the many applications of the "Regulex".

Before expounding finally the fundamental principle of the Autodyne, let us first investigate the path leading from conventional d-c generators, which permit only manual regulation, to one which, in *Fig. 7b*, automatically maintains constant the load current, and therefrom to the amplifier generator in *Fig. 7c*, which represents a generalized form. It is at the same time intended to establish the analogies existing in this respect between d-c generators and rotary converters and to find, on the basis of these analogies, the transition from SCHENFER's rotary converter *(Fig. 2a)*, permitting manual voltage regulation only, to the Autodyne.

In the case of a d-c generator provided with a single winding supplied separately (winding 2 of the generator in *Fig. 7a*, with winding 3 eliminated), the load current can obviously not be independent of the load resistance, since, for any given field current, both the main flux and the emf between the brushes A and B are also given. Consequently, disregarding the comparatively small armature reaction (and resistance), voltage cannot be changed automatically

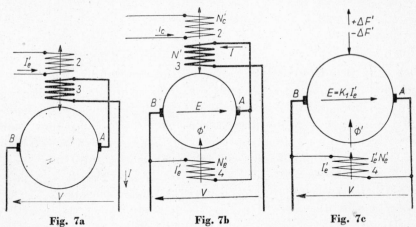

Fig. 7a   Fig. 7b   Fig. 7c

by the current. SCHENFER's machine according to *Fig. 2a* may be considered as the analogous case in the field of rotary converters. The magnet system is, however, different from that of d-c generators, inasmuch as the magnetic flux in the latter always acts along the same axis and must be modified for voltage regulation, while for this purpose it must be displaced in SHENFER's machine and yet maintains its constant magnitude.

Complete analogy can at the same time be recognized, inasmuch as the change in voltage is due, in SCHENFER's machine also, essentially to the change in a flux acting along a definite axis, to the change namely in the direct-axis component of the constant flux to be turned. This analogy leads to the subsequent one, according to which the voltage between the brushes of SCHENFER's machine is produced by almost any exciting current and does not change under the influence of the current. The magnitude of the load current must therefore depend on the external resistance.

Let us return now to the generator in *Fig. 7a*, and investigate whether the desired solution can be attained, e.g., by the aid of a counter-compound winding 3, since the emf and the voltage now decrease as the current is increased, which necessarily reduces the degree of current increase at diminished load resistance. It will readily be perceived, however, that the constancy of current I cannot be ensured by this connection either, since with a constant current I and a given field current I_e the voltage V cannot change, which, in fact, would be the basic requirement for the constancy of current I even at a change of the load resistance.

The analogous case for rotary converters would be obtained if windings carrying current were added in the direct axis, or the quadrature axis, or both axes, in addition to the separately supplied mmfs F_e and F'_e mentioned before. The windings could in these cases be arranged without difficulty to act in such a manner that by increasing the load current — owing to their mmfs now representing part of the total mmf —, the direction of the latter should change so as to cause a corresponding reduction in voltage. Similar machines have actually been suggested by SCHENFER for special applications. Yet it will be observed again that this method is not suitable either for ensuring the constancy of I at any arbitrary value of V, inasmuch as for given values of F_e and F'_e a well-defined angle β is obviously obtained at a given value of I. Since, however, the values γ and V_{1res} are already determined in Eq. (3a), a single value of V can only pertain to the given value of I.

Let us return now to the d-c generator in *Fig. 7a* and investigate the conditions resulting, if a shunt winding 4 is added to the windings 2 and 3 of the generator *(Fig. 7b)*.

The operation principle of this machine may be made clear by a somewhat idealized conception, i.e. by first investigating a generator having one shunt winding 4 *(Fig. 7c)* only. Let the speed of the rotor be constant and suppose the flux Φ' between points a and a' on the no-load characteristic *(Fig. 8)* as well as the emf E (or the internal voltage) on the d-c side to be proportional to the exciting mmf $I'_e N'_e$, i.e. $E = K_1 I'_e$. Neglecting, as before, the voltage drops in the armature and on the brushes, the emf E will be equal to the voltage drops $K_2 I'_e$ on the shunt winding. With the constants K_1 and K_2 chosen to be equal, the straight line $K_2 I'_e$ fully coincides with the straight part between a and a' of the no-load curve, and the generator can give whatever corresponds to values E and Φ', because E always produces current I'_e necessary for establishing flux Φ'

which, in turn, generates the given emf E. In that way the flux Φ' and the emf E are in a state of indifferent equilibrium.

By producing a small additional mmf $+\varDelta F'$ *(Fig. 7c)*, by which the no-load curve is shifted somewhat to the left *(Fig. 8, dotted line)*, the generator becomes self-excited, in consequence of which the emf increases to the value E_{max}, that is, to the height

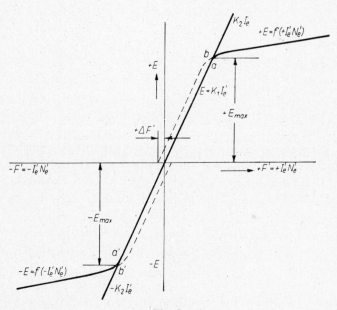

Fig. 8

of point b in, which the shifted curve and the straight line $K_2 I'_e$ intersect. Consequently, the appearance of a small signal $+\varDelta F'$ causes the flux Φ' and the emf E to leave the formerly indifferent state of equilibrium and the emf E to increase to the limit value E_{max}, whereby the latter is practically independent of the magnitude of $+\varDelta F'$, determining only the velocity by which E grows up to E_{max}. Obviously, when a mmf impulse $-\varDelta F'$ in the opposite direction (arrow directed downwards in *Fig. 7c*) appears, the emf will change its sense and reach the value $-E_{max}$ *(Fig. 8)*.

Add now to winding 4 *(Fig. 7c)*, the windings 2 and 3 carrying, in the direction shown, the currents i_c and I, respectively, and with the number of turns N'_c and N', respectively *(Fig. 7b)*. Assuming $I'N' = i_c N'_c$, the adding will not cause any mmf impulse $\pm \varDelta F'$, and therefore the emf E and the flux $\varPhi'$ will keep in the state of indifferent equilibrium when I remains constant. If, on the contrary, I increases or decreases by $\pm \varDelta I$, the signals $\mp \varDelta F'$ appear and diminish or enlarge $\varPhi'$ and E, until I equals again the value $i_c N'_c/N'$.

In this way the automatic stabilization of current I at the reference value

$$I = i_c \frac{N'_c}{N}$$

can be achieved by the aid of control windings 2 and 3.

It can easily be understood that, instead of comparing the quantities IN' and $i_c N'_c$, any other electrically representable quantities $\varPi_1$ and $\varPi_2$ may be compared, on the basis of the circuit diagram in *Fig. 7c*, if the control windings are chosen accordingly. Beside the interdependence described above between the appearance of signal $\pm \varDelta F'$ and the emf variation $\pm \varDelta E$ caused by it, it is sufficient to establish an external connection (feedback) by the aid of control windings (as for example 2 and 3) between $\pm \varDelta E$ and the signals $\mp \varDelta F'$, whereby these signals act in a direction to eliminate the primary signals $\pm \varDelta F'$.

The theory described above holds only if some disturbing phenomena are neglected, as for instance the voltage drop originated by the load current or the deviation of the curve $E = f(I'_e N'_e)$ from the straight line $K_1 I'_e$, etc. The presence of these phenomena may introduce some inaccuracies in the automatic stabilization. The accuracy may be increased by finding means for diminishing the influence of these disturbances.

Hence the following principal conditions may be set for developing generators similar to those in *Fig. 7b*.

1. Let us envisage a basic connection diagram in which the emf E and the voltage V are practically in a state of indifferent equilibrium, which is disturbed by the appearance of the smallest additional mmf $\pm \varDelta F'$ tending to vary the voltage to the limit values $\pm V_{max}$.

2. Let us envisage a feedback between these variations and the signals $\mp \varDelta F'$ (beside the interdependence signals $\pm \varDelta F'$ and the variation of the voltage caused by it). This will be achieved by using control windings, whereby the variation of voltage should provoke signals of the mmf opposite to those mentioned in point 1.

3. Let us eliminate, as completely as possible, the factors apt to cause inaccuracies in the control.

These ways of transforming a d-c generator into a generator capable of stabilizing certain quantities are, in many respects, similar to the methods of transforming the generalized rotary converter into an autodyne.

The first step in this direction will be described in the following chapter.

CHAPTER 4

CREATION OF THE MAGNETIC SYSTEM OF THE AUTODYNE OPERATING IN A STATE OF INDIFFERENT EQUILIBRIUM

Suppose that in a rotary converter the stator windings and the mmfs F'_e and F_e belonging to the former are absent.

In this case the resulting flux $\overline{\Phi_{1\text{res}}}$ is produced by the mmf of the magnetizing phase current $\overline{I_{m\text{res}}}$, fed to the armature from the three-phase supply circuit, and the phase emf $\overline{E_{1\text{res}}}$, induced by flux $\overline{\Phi_{1\text{res}}}$, equilibrates the terminal voltage $V_{1\text{res}}$ *(Fig. 9)*.

Let us assume the flux $\overline{\Phi_{1\text{res}}}$ to rotate, relative to the armature, anticlockwise, with the synchronous speed

$$n_s = \frac{60f}{p}$$

and the armature itself to revolve clockwise. Now, three cases can be distinguished, depending on the speed of the armature:

1. If $n < n_s$, the flux $\overline{\Phi_{1r\ s}}$ rotates antirclockwise, with the speed $n_s - n$ *(Fig. 9)*.

As the angle β varies proportionally to time, the emf E according to Eq. (3) varies sinusoidally. Hence between the brushes A and B, an alternating voltage $V_\sim$ arises with the frequency

$$\frac{p(n_s - n)}{60}$$

2. If $n > n_s$, the flux $\overline{\Phi_{1\text{res}}}$ rotates clockwise with the speed $n - n_s$ *(Fig. 10)*. Consequently, an alternating voltage $V_\sim$ again arises between the brushes A and B, with the frequency

$$\frac{p(n - n_s)}{60}$$

3. If $n = n_s$, the flux Φ_{1res} does not rotate, and the angle β remains constant; therefore the voltage arising between the brushes A and B *(Fig. 11)* has the constant value

$$V = V_{max} \cos \beta = c_1 V_{1res} \cos \beta \tag{10}$$

where V attains the maximal value V_{max} when $\beta = 0$.

The third case seems at first sight somewhat unreal, because in the absence of stator windings, no torque can be produced to

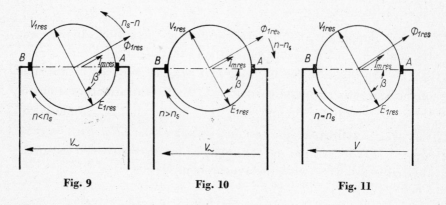

Fig. 9   **Fig. 10**   **Fig. 11**

counteract the frictional torque. Consequently, the armature cannot rotate synchronously.

Meanwhile let us assume that the frictional torque T_f is eliminated by some means and no other imaginable internal torques are acting upon the armature, as, e.g., those arising from hysteresis and due to the different permeance in different directions.

In this case the armature maintains its speed n_s, to which it has been accelerated by whatever means, and the values β and V therefore remain constant. Hereby the flux $\overline{\Phi_{1res}}$ may assume any possible position, depending upon the moment when the armature reaches synchronism, that is, the flux will be in a state of indifferent equilibrium and the voltage V may assume every possible value within the limits $\pm V_{max}$. Thus an analogy can be detected between the generator as shown in Fig. 7c and the machine as shown in Fig. 11, in spite of their different physical shape.

The same analogy can be observed in the fact that the voltage of both the generator of Fig. 7c and the system shown in Fig. 11, which is with regard to voltage V in, a state of indifferent equilibrium, reacts *very sensibly to the appearance of an arbitrary additional mmf. In the latter system, this is achieved by the torque provoked by the additional mmf.*

When investigating these phenomena, we shall choose the following well-known fact for our point of departure : if some arbitrary mmf is added in the stator or the rotor of the rotary converter to the mmf established by the exciting current, the mains is practically short-circuited with respect to the emf due to this additional mmf, because $\overline{V_{1r\ s}}$ is already equilibrated by $\overline{E_{1r\ s}}$. Therefore, the armature will take a three-phase current from the mains, called in the following "compensating current", because its mmf practically compensates the above-mentioned additional mmf.

It follows therefrom that by creating the impulse of the mmf $-\Delta F'$ *(Fig. 12)* in the stator, a compensating current

$$+\Delta I'_{1C} = c_2\, \Delta F' \tag{11}$$

(where c_2 is constant) arises in the armature winding. The direction of the component $c_2\, \Delta F' \sin \beta$ of this current and that of the vector $\overline{V_{1res}}$ coincide, whereby this component represents a motor current producing an accelerating torque. The latter causes the speed of the armature n to increase beyond the synchronous speed n_s, that is,

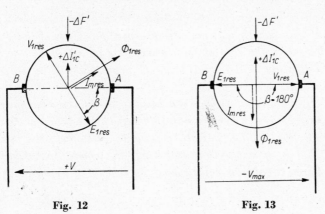

Fig. 12   Fig. 13

the characteristic conditions of *Fig. 10* are obtained and the vectors $\overline{V_{1res}}$, $\overline{E_{1res}}$, $\overline{\Phi_{1res}}$ and $\overline{I_{mres}}$ rotate clockwise until they reach the position *(Fig. 13)* in which $\Delta I'_{1C}$ has no more active component. As it may be seen, the voltage V changes in this case from $+V$ to $-V_{max}$.

In the presence of a contrary impulse $+\Delta F'$ generating a braking torque in the armature, the vectors $\overline{V_{1r\ s}}$, $\overline{E_{1r\ s}}$, $\overline{\Phi_{1r\ s}}$ and $\overline{I_{mr\ s}}$ will rotate anticlockwise from the position corresponding to *Fig. 14* to the position according to *Fig. 15*, whereby the voltage V will vary from $+V$ to $+V_{max}$.

In this way it becomes evident that even unimportant impulses of the stator mmf $\pm\Delta F'$ can, by means of torques provoked by them, cause considerable changes in the value of V.

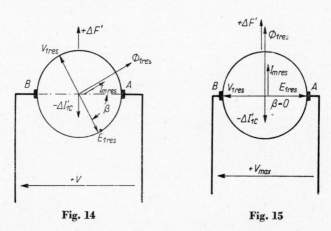

Fig. 14   **Fig. 15**

Moreover, as in the generator of Fig. 7c, the values $\pm V_{max}$, to which V approaches, will not depend upon the values of these impulses $\pm\Delta F'$, but only the rate of these variations will be governed by them, as the acceleration or deceleration of the armature will be proportionate to $\pm\Delta F' \sin\beta$.

It follows that we have succeeded in producing a basic connection for the rotary converter ensuring an interdependence between the impulses $\pm\Delta F'$ and the voltage variations due to them between the brushes A and B, i.e. a connection fulfilling the conditions mentioned in Chapter 2, and capable of substituting the scheme of the generator shown in Fig. 7c.

CHAPTER 5

AN AUTODYNE STABILIZING THE LOAD CURRENT
AT A CONTROLLABLE REFERENCE VALUE

On the basis of the system investigated, quite a number of different connections can be conceived, satisfying the conditions mentioned in *Chapter 2*. Definite quantities can, in the same manner as with the d-c generator of *Fig. 7c*, be automatically stabilized by adding to the machine, shown in *Fig. 11*, stator control windings in which the variations of voltage V — caused by the impulses $\pm \Delta F'$ owing to the said interdependence — produce, by means of some arbitrary external feedback, impulses of the mmf $\mp \Delta F'$, opposed to these impulses $\pm \Delta F'$.

Let us examine the following example: we want to produce an autodyne *(Fig. 16)* in which, similarly to the generator of *Fig. 7b*, the load current I stabilizes itself automatically at any definite and continuously controllable reference level, independently of the value of the external load resistance. For this purpose, the same control windings are to be added to the circuit diagram of *Fig. 11* as those added to the circuit diagram of the generator *(Fig. 7c)*. Thus the feedback produced by these windings will be the same between the variations of voltage and the variations of the mmfs. In this case the same load curve is obtained:

$$I = i_c \frac{N'_c}{N'} \qquad (12)$$

The following considerations will make it clear that the autodyne of *Fig. 16* really controls the current according to this law. Should the mmf $i_c N'_c$ act alone, it would cause a compensating current $c_2 i_c N'_c$, which would yield together with the voltage $E_{1\text{res}}$ the generator power

$$- 3\, E_{1\text{res}}\, c_2\, i_c\, N'_c \sin \beta$$

Similarly, the mmf IN' would yield a motor power

$$3 E_{1\text{res}} c_2 IN' \sin \beta$$

Under steady-state conditions, when $n = n_s$, the algebraic sum of all powers and torques concerned has to equal zero. Thus the power produced by the current $c_2 i_c N'_c$ equals the power of current $c_2 IN'$. In this way we obtain the equation

$$(i_c N'_c - IN') \sin \beta = 0 \qquad (13)$$

Moreover, we assume that no internal torques are acting upon the armature, i.e. the generator power produced by the current and the corresponding braking torque are exactly equal to the motor

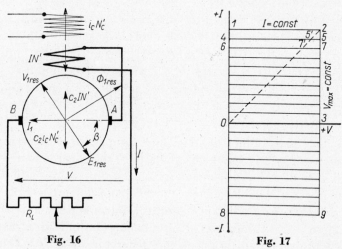

Fig. 16   Fig. 17

power produced by the phase current I_1 and to the corresponding accelerating torque, respectively. This current I_1 compensates in the armature winding for the magnetic reaction of the current I.

By excluding the singular case where $\beta = 0$, i.e. where neither the mmf $i_c N'_c$ nor the mmf IN' produces an active power or the corresponding torque, the Eq. (13) will have the solution represented by Eq. (12). In this case the autodyne indeed controls itself in such a way as to cause the difference between the said mmfs to disappear, i.e. according to the law

$$\pm \varDelta F' = 0 \qquad (14)$$

In this way the control windings ensure in the given connection of the autodyne the same automatic stabilization as in the gener-

*ator of Fig. 7b, although the physical function of these windings is quite
different in the two cases. In the case of the generator (Fig. 7b), they
compare the fluxes provoked by them, while in case of the autodyne
(Fig. 16) they compare between each other the torques provoked by them.*

Thus the current I is maintained at the reference value
$i_c N_c'/N'$ and, what is more, at any arbitrary value of the load resistance
R_L, being smaller than $V_{max} N'/i_c N_c$, including the case of $R_L = 0$, i.e.
of short circuit, where $V = 0$. By increasing the resistance R_L to
the limit value given above, the voltage V
increases automatically until V_{max} is reached.
Meanwhile β decreases to zero, beyond which
the autodyne loses its ability to control. In
reality, when R_L increases further and the
current I decreases, the mmf $i_c N_c' - IN'$
arising thereby, is no longer able to control,
because, when $\beta = 0$, the compensating alternating current produces no more active power
and provokes no torque. At the same time
$\overline{\Phi_{1res}}$ acts along the direct axis and the autodyne becomes an ordinary converter, which
involves that the characteristic $I = $ constant,
i.e. the straight line $1-2$ *(Fig. 17)*, passes
over to the characteristic $V = V_{max} =$
$= $ constant, i.e. to the straight line $2-3$.

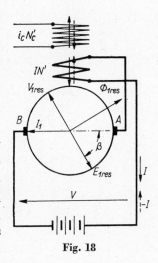

Fig. 18

By decreasing the control current i_c, we can reduce the
current I (e.g. obtain, instead of the straight line $1-2$, the lines
$4-5'$ or $6-7'$ etc.). By adequately increasing the resistance R_L, these
straight lines may be extended until points 5, 7, etc. If $i_c = 0$, the
current I decreases even in short circuit to zero (point 0).

If the resistance R_L is relaced by a storage battery
according to *Fig. 18*, the autodyne ensures the constancy of charging
current I, while the voltage V increases automatically in the course
of charging. When reaching the limit value $V = V_{max}$, the battery
current falls to zero (straight line $2-3$ in *Fig. 17*). The value of the
charging current does not depend upon V within the values $0 < V <$
$< V_{max}$, i.e. the same autodyne can charge batteries with different
voltages. The charging current I may be decreased by reducing the
current i_c, and becomes zero when the latter is diminished to zero
(e.g. characteristics $4-5$, $6-7$ and $0-3$). Moreover, the direction

of the current I may be reversed by changing the direction of current i_c, and the sense of the mmf $i_c N'_c$ (the relevant arrow in *Fig. 18* is marked by a dotted line). The mmf $i_c N'_c + IN'$ provoked there creates an accelerating torque causing the vector $\overline{E_{1\text{res}}}$ to rotate farther clockwise and to pass a position, in which the emf E of the autodyne equals the emf of the battery. Meanwhile the value of current I decreases till zero. The mmf acting in the stator still has the value

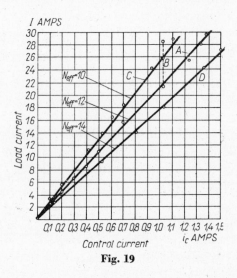

Fig. 19

$i_c N'_c$, and causes a further clockwise rotation of vector $\overline{E_{1\text{res}}}$. Consequently, the emf E of the autodyne will be higher than that of the battery. Hence current I and the mmf IN' change their direction (dotted vectors) and the current grows to the value $- i_c N'_c/N'$ (e.g. according to the straight line 8—9 in *Fig. 17*), at which the effect of the mmf $i_c N'_c$ produced by current i_c is completely neutralized by the aid of the once opposite mmf IN' created by current I. *In this way the autodyne ensures the discharge of the battery with constant discharging current. The machine is no longer a rectifier converting a-c power into d-c power but an inverted converter converting d-c power into a-c power, that is, it supplies energy taken from the battery back to the mains. In this way the forming of a battery is possible without a rheostat.*

Fig. 19 shows some control characteristics of an experimental model of autodyne, constructed in the Moscow Institute of

Transport Engineers (MITE), according to *Fig. 16*, with a different number of the "effective" turns on the direct-axis series control winding. In order to ensure the possibility of varying the mmf IN' continuously, the brushes in the machine mentioned were shifted from the geometrically neutral position. This created an armature mmf proportional to current I and acting in the direct axis. If the algebraic sum of this mmf and that of the winding N' is divided by the current I, we obtain the number of "effective" turns of the machine tested.

As can be seen, all these characteristics are straight lines, intersecting the coordinate system at the origin in, conformity with Eq. (12), in which by diminishing the number of "effective" turns, the slope of the straight lines increases accordingly.

CHAPTER 6

CREATING IMPULSES OF STATOR MMF
TO ENSURE SYNCHRONOUS OPERATION.
THE STARTING OF THE AUTODYNE

Let us investigate how the synchronizing torques are produced, when the flux is in indifferent equilibrium. Without synchronizing torques, the operation of no synchronous machine, like the autodyne, is stable.

The synchronous operation of the rotary converter, as shown in *Fig. 3*, is conditioned mainly by the fact that mmfs F_e' and F_e are established in the stator.

Thus the stator flux $\overline{\Phi_{1res}}$ produces not only the steady-state torque equilibrating in synchronism the frictional torque, but also the dynamic synchronizing torque at every attempt of the rotor to pass over, for whatever reason, into asynchronous run. Here and hereafter the term of positive or negative slip of the armature is understood to be an operation condition, at which the speed of the armature n is lower or higher than the synchronous one n_s.

In case of a positive slip the vector $\overline{V_{1res}}$ travels the angle $\Delta\gamma$ anticlockwise with speed Δn. But as vector $\overline{E_{1res}}$, closely joined to the stator flux $\overline{\Phi_{1res}}$, meanwhile remains unchanged, there arises — as already mentioned above — beside the current I_f provoked by the frictional torque, a synchronizing three-phase current ΔI_s *(Fig. 3)*. The flux produced by the latter induces an additional voltage, equal in magnitude to $V_{1res}\,\Delta\gamma$ and perpendicular to $\overline{V_{1res}}$. The accelerating torque ΔT created by ΔI_s and by the stator flux acts as a synchronizing element. Oscillations of vector V_{1res} arise round its steady-state position, whereby the direction of current ΔI_s and that of torque ΔT vary with the sign of the angle difference $\Delta\gamma$. These oscillations decay rapidly when damping torques are present.

The autodyne in which the stator winding is missing has quite an other aspect. In case of a positive slip, the rotor travels the angle $\Delta\beta$, and the vector $\overline{V_{1res}}$, as well as the vector $\overline{I_{mres}}$ lags behind by 90° and slips to the position shown by dotted lines. Therefore also the flux $\overline{\Phi_{1res}}$ *(Fig. 20)* produced by current $\overline{I_{mres}}$ slips until the position shown by the dotted line, and no dynamic torques are produced. When the rotor slips, both the vector $\overline{V_{1res}}$ and the vector $\overline{E_{1res}}$, opposed to the former, will slip, in consequence of which neither a current ΔI_s, nor a torque ΔT will arise.

As shown above, the resultant mmf in the autodyne, according to *Fig. 16*, is zero in steady, state, i.e. no exciting mmf nor any other mmfs are, after all, acting in the stator.

Let us investigate by what the synchronous operation of such a machine is secured.

The absence of an exciting mmf closely joined with the stator excludes the possibility of synchronizing the armature, as in the scheme of Fig. 3. Meanwhile this permits to achieve the synchronization according to a completely new principle, consisting in creating synchronizing torques by the aid of impulses $\mp\Delta F'$, produced by control windings.

Suppose that the armature of the autodyne *(Fig. 20)* begins to slip. In such a case the vectors $\overline{\Phi_{1res}}, \overline{E_{1res}}$ and $\overline{I_{mres}}$ travel the angle $-\Delta\beta$ until they reach the position marked by dotted lines. Assume now that in the stator, where at synchronous operations no resultant mmfs are present, a mmf impulse $-\Delta F'$ is created when the rotor slips. This mmf would provoke a compensating current $c_2\,\Delta F'$, the active component of which $c_2\,\Delta F'\sin\beta$ corresponds to a motor power, and would create an accelerating torque, in the case given a synchronizing one ΔT.

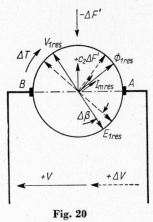

Fig. 20

The synchronism ensured by mmf impulses is achieved by the above-mentioned feedback between $\Delta\beta$ and $\Delta F'$: each variation $\Delta\beta$ provokes an impulse $\Delta F'$, responsible for the torque ΔT counteracting the variation of angle β.

In reality while the vector V_{1res} travels a small angle $-\Delta\beta$, the magnitude of the quadrature-axis component $V_{1res}\cos\beta$ varies by the value $V_{1\text{res}} \sin \beta \, \varDelta\beta$, and the voltage between the brushes A and B, which is proportional to it, changes by the value

$$\varDelta V = c_1 V_{1\text{res}} \sin \beta \, \varDelta\beta \qquad (15)$$

if we assume for the present that the current $I = 0$. (The direction $+ \varDelta V$ is marked in *Fig. 20* by a dotted line.)

Under load, current I varies by $\varDelta I$ with the variation of the voltage V. In *Chapter 19* it will be shown that, by neglecting the influence of self-inductivity,

$$\varDelta I = \frac{c_1 V_{1\text{res}} \sin \beta \, \varDelta\beta}{\varSigma R_a + R_L}$$

where R_L is the resistance of the load and $\varSigma R_a$ a quantity called the resultant resistance of the autodyne. Thus in the autodyne *(Fig. 16)* the mmf impulse

$$c_1 V_{1\text{res}} \sin \beta \, \varDelta\beta \, \frac{N'}{\varSigma R_a + R_L}$$

provokes a torque.

By taking into consideration $E_{1\text{res}} \approx V_{1\text{res}}$ we find that the impulse of the compensating current, created by the mmf impulse mentioned above, represents with the voltage $V_{1\text{res}}$ or emf $E_{1\text{res}}$ a synchronizing power in relation to the unit angle deviation $\varDelta\beta$

$$\frac{\varDelta P_s}{\varDelta\beta} = \frac{3 c_1 c_2 N' V_{1\text{res}}^2 \sin^2 \beta}{\varSigma R_a + R_L} \qquad (16\text{a})$$

It is of interest to note that the value of the synchronizing torque, established on the basis of the new principle, depends upon quantities entirely different from the one in the rotary converter in *Fig. 3*.

By denoting the effective number of armature turns of the rotary converter by N_{eff}, the ratio of the mmf $\varDelta I_s N_{\text{eff}}$ to the voltage $V_{1\text{res}} \varDelta\gamma$, induced by its flux, equals the ratio of the mmf F_e' to the quadrature-axis component E_1. Since in case of $\beta = 0$, E_1 equals $E_{1\text{res}}$ and F_e' equals $F_{e\max}'$, we obtain

$$\frac{F_{e\max}'}{E_{1\text{res}}} = \frac{\varDelta I_s N_{\text{eff}}}{V_{1\text{res}} \varDelta\gamma} \qquad (17)$$

In this way the ratio $\Delta P_s/\Delta\gamma$ of the synchronizing power to the unit angle $\Delta\gamma$ in the case of rotary converters will be

$$\frac{\Delta P_s}{\Delta\gamma} = \frac{3\,E_{1res}\,\Delta I_s}{\Delta\gamma} = 3\,E_{1res}\,F'_{emax}\,\frac{V_{1res}}{E_{1res}N_{eff}} \approx \frac{3\,E_{1res}\,F'_{emax}}{N_{eff}} \quad (16b)$$

and since

$$E_{1res} \equiv \Phi_{1res}\,N_{eff}\,n_s \tag{18}$$

$\Delta P_s/\Delta\gamma$ will be proportional to $\Phi_{1res}\,F'_{emax}\,n_s$.

Obviously, the magnitude of synchronizing power and that of the corresponding synchronizing torque are in the rotary converter, at a given flux, proportional to the exciting mmf, i. e. they grow with the air gap, while in the autodyne, according to the circuit diagram in Fig. 16, they are independent of these quantities.

In the converter *(Fig. 3)* the synchronizing torque, at a fixed flux and mmf, is given, while in the autodyne, according to the circuit diagram of *Fig. 16*, it can be enlarged by an adequate choice of the number of turns in the control winding.

It is also of theoretical and practical interest that, in the machine of *Fig. 16*, the synchronizing torque depends on the resistance of the load circuit. Consequently, when this latter is short-circuited, the synchronizing torque will reach its highest value. The smaller the resulting armature resistance — which is generally very low in the rotary converter — the higher the synchronizing torque will be.

It follows therefrom that by the adequate choice of the ratio between the variation of voltage V *and the mmf impulse of the control winding provoked thereby, synchronizing torques substantially greater than in the rotary converter may readily be obtained.*

In connection with the above, the problem of starting has to be discussed.

In *Chapter 4* the armature of the autodyne was assumed to be in rotation, although it was not described how this machine starts.

In this respect the autodyne behaves like a rotary converter with damping winding. The autodyne has, in fact, beside the control and regulating windings, other windings arranged along the direct and quadrature axis and fed from the brushes of the commutator (the purpose of these windings will be explained in detail in *Chapters 12* and *13*). After connecting the armature at rest to the mains, the flux

4*

$\overline{\Phi}_{1\text{res}}$ rotates at a speed n_s anticlockwise and generates voltage
in the windings. As the resistance of the armature is negligible in
comparison to the resistance of the windings mentioned above, the
latter are practically short-circuited for the said voltage through the
armature. Consequently, the currents produced by these voltages
create a torque analogous to the starting torque of an inverse asynchronous motor. The voltage between the brushes of the commutator
is known to vary during the start of the converter periodically with
the frequency

$$\frac{p(n_s - n)}{60}$$

diminishing from the value

$$\frac{p n_s}{60}$$

to a small value, which depends upon the frictional torque. On
the other hand, in the autodyne, as assumed above, this torque
is eliminated, as will be explained in *Chapter 13*. That is why, during
asynchronous start, the autodyne accelerates practically to full synchronism, whereafter the flux (as described in *Chapter 4*) assumes
a definite, practically fixed position in space. At start the control
and regulating windings are not connected. Consequently, immediately after starting, the position of the flux is an arbitrary one,
and so are the polarity of the commutator brushes and the direction
of voltage V. If, however, on reaching synchronism, one of the direct-
axis and one of the quadrature-axis windings are for a short time
connected in such a way as to make their resulting mmf act in the same
direction as in *Fig. 2a*, the flux will take the position represented in
Figs. 2a and *16* and the brushes obtain the desired polarity. Sub-
sequently, the switching on of the control and regulating windings
of the autodyne, according to the corresponding circuit diagram,
creates a particular, synchronizing impulse above described, characteristic of every autodyne. These force the flux $\overline{\Phi}_{1\text{res}}$ to maintain or
resume its position which, according to the law of self-regulation,
corresponds to the given operation conditions of the autodyne.

     Fig. 21 shows an oscillogram of starting the autodyne
AZ 140/72, the three-phase line-to-line voltage of the mains being
$V_{1\text{res}} = 380$ V.

As shown by the oscillogram, on connecting the sliprings of the autodyne to the a-c mains, an asynchronous start is obtained (the period interval of the change in voltage V increases whenever the slip decreases). When the slip reaches the value $s = 0{\cdot}0555$, i.e. when the number of revolutions is

$$n_2 = (1 - s)\, n_1 = 0{\cdot}9445 \cdot 1500 = 1420 \text{ rpm}$$

the machine is pulled automatically into synchronism. The asynchronous start before reaching synchronism takes 8 seconds, while the time necessary to synchronization is $0{\cdot}5$ seconds.

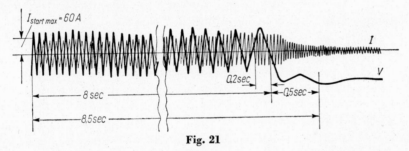

Fig. 21

The highest value of current during asynchronous start was 60 A, its effective value being $42{\cdot}5$ A, i.e. 177 per cent of the rated a-c value 27 A. After having reached synchronism, the alternating current rapidly diminished.

CHAPTER 7

SOME GENERALIZED CONCLUSIONS

The considerations in *Chapters 5* and *6* refer to the circuit diagram of the autodyne according to *Figs. 16* and *18*. Nevertheless they enable us to draw some conclusions concerning all possible schemes of the autodyne and are therefore of general importance.

By investigating the analogy between the autodyne and the generator shown in *Fig. 7c*, some additional differences should be taken into consideration as follows.

1. In the generator of *Fig. 7c*, the flux per pole always acts along the same direct axis, may have an arbitrary value, and is always in a state of indifferent equilibrium. On the other hand, the spatial fundamental Φ_{1res} of the flux in the autodyne has practically always the same value, but may take any position, remaining in the state of indifferent equilibrium.

2. In the generator of *Fig. 7c*, E is generated by the total flux. In the autodyne, E is generated by the part Φ' of the flux, which acts along the direct axis, while its magnitude is determined by the position of the spatial fundamental $\overline{\Phi_{1res}}$.

3. In the generator shown in *Fig. 7c*, the impulses $\pm\Delta F'$ produce additional flux, disturbing the state of indifferent equilibrium of the flux Φ' and cause thereby great changes in its value. In the autodyne the impulses $\pm\Delta F'$ produce additional torques accelerating or decelerating the armature, and disturb thereby the state of indifferent equilibrium of the spatial fundamental Φ_{1res}, causing considerable changes in its direction.

4. In the generator of *Fig. 7c*, the variation of voltage is produced by the changes in the value of the total, flux as a consequence of the appearance of the impulses $\pm\Delta F'$. In the autodyne, this is produced by the variation of that part of the flux which acts along the direct axis, while the variation of the direct-axis flux is

determined by the changes in the position of the spatial fundamental $\overline{\Phi_{1\text{res}}}$.

5. In the generator of *Fig. 7b*, the mmfs of the control windings act on the voltage through the fluxes provoked by them. In the autodyne, however, they act through the accelerating or decelerating torques produced by them.

6. In order to establish a state of indifferent equilibrium between the flux and the voltage in the generator of *Fig. 7c*, it is necessary to eliminate the influence of such factors as voltage drop or saturation etc. In the autodyne the internal torques, first of all the frictional torque, are to be eliminated for this purpose.

There is also a difference, of both theoretical and practical interest, in the choice of the possible connections of control windings, determining the different possible characteristics.

For the autodyne, any circuit diagram similar to the control type machine developed on the basis of the generator *(Fig. 7c)* can, in principle, be produced. There are great many schemes of this kind.

In fact the essential part of the circuit diagram of *Fig. 16* is that the algebraic sum of the mmfs, produced by the windings N'_c and N' should, at any arbitrary voltage V, be zero, i. e. that no difference $\pm \Delta F'$, of the mmfs, disturbing the state of equilibrium, should arise. Obviously, any number of such circuit diagrams can be designed.

While, for instance, in the scheme of the autodyne in *Fig. 16*, an mmf proportional to the load current is compared to the reference mmf, any given electrical or electrically measurable quantity Π_2 can, in the general case of the autodyne, be compared to any other electrical or electrically measurable quantity Π_1, i. e. the autodyne can stabilize them at a determined controllable reference value, according to the law

$$\Pi_1 = \Pi_2$$

Instead of two such windings as N'_c and N' *(Fig. 16)*, a single winding may be used, the mmf of which is controlled automatically to be zero, meaning, in the given case, that the current in this winding should be zero. By connecting to such a winding a voltage proportional to the difference of the quantities Π_1 and Π_2, the autodyne will control in a way to ensure the difference to be zero, according to the law $\Pi_1 = \Pi$.

Even by disregarding the possibility of adding to the mmfs of windings N_c' and N', or to the mmf of a winding substituting the former, several other mmf's obtained in different ways, and of changing thereby the law of control, it is obvious that the number of schemes for the construction of the autodyne similar to the generator in Fig. 7c is extremely high.

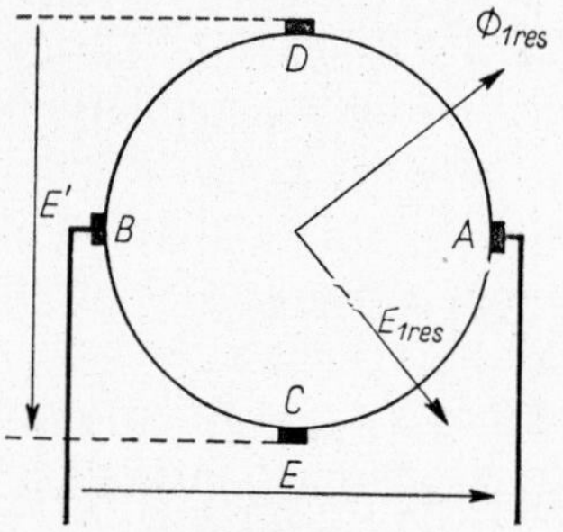

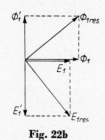

Fig. 22a

The autodyne, however, may be constructed also on the basis of many other schemes that cannot be derived from the generator (Fig. 7c).

Firstly, the control windings in the generator *(Fig. 7c)* may be arranged along one axis only, while in the autodyne they can be situated along different axes, in consequence of which the number of possible connections and characteristics is very much enlarged.

Secondly, the impulse of the mmf in the generator *(Fig. 7c)* at no load may be obtained only by varying the voltage V between the brushes situated in the quadrature axis. In the autodyne, an mmf impulse can be obtained not only from the quadrature-axis brushes $A - B$, but also from the direct-axis brushes $C - D$ *(Fig. 22a)*. When considered from the operational angle, the quadrature-axis brushes are, in fact, the main ones, the direct axis-brushes being the auxiliary ones.

Fig. 22b

Let us recall that the emf E_1 *(Fig. 22b)* generated by the flux Φ_1', in the phase winding corresponds to the emf $E = c_1 E_1$ between the brushes $A - B$ on the d-c side. It is obvious that, similarly, the emf E_1' generated in the phase winding by the flux Φ_1 corresponds to the emf

$$E' = c_1 E_1' \tag{19}$$

acting between the brushes $C - D$ on the d-c side. At no load $E_{1res} \cong V_{1res}$ whence

$$E \cong c_1 V_{1res} \cos \beta$$

and

$$E' \cong c_1 V_{1res} \sin \beta$$

Thus the angle variation $-\Delta\beta$ in the autodyne generates not only a voltage variation $c_1 V_{1\text{res}} \sin \beta \, \Delta\beta$ between the main brushes $A - B$, but also a voltage variation $-c_1 V_{1\text{res}} \cos \beta \, \Delta\beta$ between the auxiliary brushes $C - D$.

In this way it becomes possible to produce the feedback not only by means of the main brushes A and B, but also through the auxiliary brushes C and D, or by using all of them. Thus the number of the different characteristics of the autodyne can be enlarged by combining the possible schemes. These combinations enable us to harness the electrodynamic forces in different ways by the particular automatism described above, from which the autodyne has obtained its name.

Finally, there is also the following possibility for the further development of the circuit diagrams and characteristics of the autodyne, beyond those of the generator in *Fig. 7c :* in the latter the load current can only be obtained from the voltage V between the quadrature-axis brushes. In the autodyne, however, the load current may, in principle, be obtained not only from the voltage V, but also from the voltage $V' \cong E'$, by adequately enlarging the auxiliary brushes C and D.

Among the different connections ensuring the feedback between ΔV and $\Delta F'$, the greatest importance should be attributed to those in which the autodyne controls a quantity Π_1 in conformity with another quantity Π_2. Such a control require ΔV to act at least upon one of these two quantities and the difference of Π_1 and Π_2 to act upon the mmf $\Delta F'$, which is then utilized as a signal for the deviation between the quantities Π_1 and Π_2. In this way it is possible to ensure, beside the synchronizing torque due to the change in angle $\Delta\beta$, the automatic control of Π_1 accordind to Π_2, which may either be constant or vary according to difinete laws. Besides, Π_1 may be a quantity referred also to any other machine. Such quantities may be: the speed and the torque of motors, the voltage or current of generators, the power factor, etc.

As to the creation of mmf impulses $\pm\Delta F'$, they will be provoked either directly or with some amplifier, by the difference of electrical quantities proportionate to the quantities Π_1 and Π_2.

From among the possible circuit diagrams and characteristics, we shall first choose for illustration some in which the control is effected along the direct axis only.

CHAPTER 8

AUTODYNES WITH SINGLE-AXIS CONTROL

In *Chapter 6* an example was shown, in which the quantity $\Pi_1 = IN'$ was controlled automatically according to quantity $\Pi_2 = i_c N'_c$. Here the comparison of the quantities Π_1 and Π_2 was achieved by two control windings. Yet the simplest single-axis control of an autodyne is the use of a single control winding N'_c.

In this connection we shall investigate several examples. The principle mentioned above is realized in *Fig. 23* ,where the voltage V of the autodyne figures as quantity Π_1, and the reference voltage V_c as quantity Π_2. In this example, winding N'_c is connected directly to the difference of these quantities. Supposing vectors $\overline{\Phi_{1\text{res}}}$ and $\overline{E_{1\text{res}}}$ assume a position in which

$$V = V_c \qquad\qquad (20)$$

i. e. $\Delta F' = 0$, then owing to the absence of torque ΔT, the armature revolves synchronously, and $\Delta\beta = 0$.

In principle the steady-state condition may be disturbed by one of the following three factors.

1. The armature alters its speed, (e. g. acceleratesby Δn). The vectors $\overline{\Phi_{1\text{res}}}$ and $\overline{E_{1\text{res}}}$ rotate clockwise, travelling the angle $\Delta\beta$, to the position shown by dotted lines. The voltage V decreases by ΔV, whereby in the winding N'_c an upward mmf is created, producing the synchronizing torque ΔT, decelerating the rotor.

2. The value of V varies because, for instance, the voltage $V_{1\text{res}}$ of the a-c side decreases by $\Delta V_{1\text{res}}$ and therefore also $E_{1\text{res}}$ diminishes by $\Delta E_{1\text{res}}$. Then V decreases by $\Delta V = c_1 \Delta E_{1\text{res}} \cos\beta$. Since V_c is an invariable reference value, the winding N'_c is now supplied by the voltage ΔV. As in the first case, the upward mmf $\Delta F'$ produces a decelerating torque ΔT, consequently vector $\overline{E_{1\text{res}}}$ rotates

anticlockwise from the position marked by a dotted arrow to the position marked by a full-line arrow and assumes the new steady-state position, when the voltage V reaches its former value.

It is clear that a similar stabilization may be achieved when V varies for any other reason (e. g. because of voltage drop in the armature, due to load).

3. By altering the value of reference voltage V_c, say increasing it by ΔV_c, again an upward impulse $\Delta F'$ of the mmf is obtained.

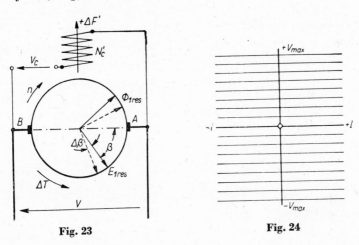

Fig. 23   Fig. 24

As in case 2, the vectors $\overline{\Phi}_{1res}$ and $\overline{E}_{1res}$ travel the angle $\Delta \beta$ counterclockwise while the voltage V increases, until the new value of $V + \Delta V = V_c + \Delta V_c$ is reached.

In this case the autodyne is, unlike the motor generator, a source of stabilized voltage, independent of any factor as, for instance, of the changes in load, in the supply voltage, or in a-c frequency, while the value of the desired voltage may be varied continuously.

In *Fig. 24* the theoretical characteristics $V = f(I)$ of this machine are plotted in form of straight lines parallel to the abscissa.

The use of a single winding may seem to be characteristic of voltage stabilization alone, while current stabilization may require two windings as shown in *Fig. 16*. In reality, however, things are quite different.

The stabilization of load current I according to a constant reference value might be achieved in principle with a single control winding N_c' as shown in *Fig. 25*.

In this case the winding is connected to the difference between the control voltage V_c, capable of being regulated, and the voltage drop across the resistance r. As in the machine shown in *Fig. 23*, the autodyne here controls in such a manner as to eliminate impulses $\pm \varDelta F'$, i. e. to avoid any current in winding N_c'. This means that the whole current I passes through the resistance r and that the relation

$$I = \frac{V_c}{r} \tag{21}$$

is valid.

On the other hand, the voltage V may also be stabilized at a reference value, according to *Fig. 16*. For this purpose the winding N' of this scheme, having but a few turns with great cross section and producing a mmf proportionate to current I, should be replaced by another winding N', having many turns with small cross section and producing a mmf proportionate to V. This condition is fulfilled, e. g., in *Fig. 26*.

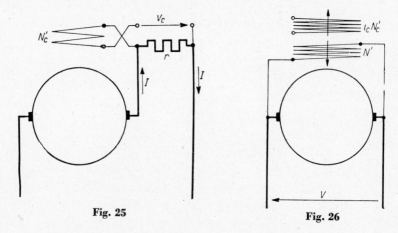

Fig. 25   Fig. 26

By denoting the resistance of winding N' by $r_{N'}$ we obtain from the equality of the mmfs in windings N' and N_c' the equation

$$V = i_c \frac{N_c' r_{N'}}{N'} \tag{22}$$

In this way the voltage in the machine *(Fig. 26)* is stabilized according to a definite reference value, capable of being varied, i. e. the schematic diagram in *Fig. 26* is, in principle, equivalent to the one in *Fig. 23*.

This, however, does not involve the equality of their importance in practice.

In the second case *(Fig. 26)*, currents flow and corresponding losses arise in both stator coils, while in the first case *(Fig. 23)*, there is only one coil which carries no current in the steady state, whereby no losses arise in it. Hence the scheme of *Fig. 23* is preferable.

Fig. 27 shows load curves $V = f(I)$ plotted against the different values of V_c in the experimental autodyne of the MITE. Here curves II and III are plotted for the case 3 referred to above. As may be seen, these curves conform in character to the theoretical curves of *Fig. 24*.

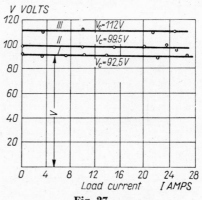

Fig. 27

Fig. 28 shows control curves $V = f(V_c)$ measured on the experimental autodynes A—2B, A—3B, and A—6B at mains voltage $V_{1res} = 220$ V. (Practically, each of these curves coincides with the corresponding ones for these different machines.)

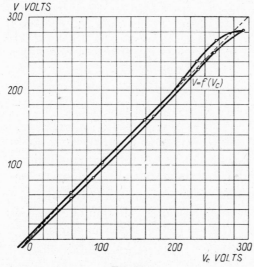

Fig. 28

Experimental results corroborate the theoretical statements of controlling the voltage of the autodyne, according to *Fig. 23*, continuously within the limits $+V_{max}$ and $-V_{max}$, by the variation of the reference voltage V_c.

The two branches of characteristic $V = f(V_c)$ can be accounted for by stator hysteresis not eliminated in these machines.

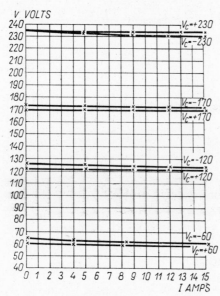

Fig. 29

Fig. 29 shows the characteristics $V = f(I)$ of the machine A—3B at different values and directions of control voltage V_c.

The above-mentioned machines A—2B, A—3B and A—6B represent three of the five test autodynes, built in the experimental factory of the Scientific Research Institute for Electrical Industry, USSR, all of them having the same power ($P = 3{,}5$ kW) and being supplied from the a-c mains (220 V). The rated voltage on the d-c side was 230 V. All machines had the same dimensions, their length was 690 mm and the outer diameter of the stator was 312 mm. *Figs. 30* and *31* show the autodyne A—2B and its armature.

The experimental autodynes built according to the circuit diagram shown here have automatic voltage control, even at instantaneous switching over from $+V_{cmax}$ to $-V_{cmax}$.

The autodyne with such characteristics can be used successfully, if the requirement is an automatic stabilization of voltage V at a continuously controllable reference value.

When feeding a d-c motor with the above-mentioned autodyne, a loss-free starting of the motor can easily be achieved by increasing the control voltage V_c from zero to V_{cmax}. By varying the value of V_c the speed of the motor can be controlled continuously. By diminishing V_c rapidly enough, the motor current changes its

Fig. 30

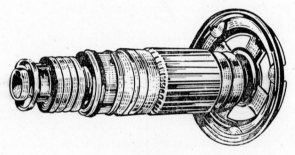

Fig. 31

direction and regenerative breaking is achieved, which results in the autodyne converting d-c power to a-c power. Therefore autodynes might be used successfully for electrical drives, where d-c motors have hitherto been supplied by motor generators.

For the mechanical characteristic $n = f(T)$ of an autodyne-supplied motor a straight line *(Fig. 32)* is obtained with a small slope due to voltage drop.

In *Fig. 33* the relation $n = f(V_c)$ is shown for the set consisting of a motor and a autodyne A—3B, operating according to *Fig. 23*.

The characteristic $n = f(V_c)$ has two branches, the hysteresis in the stator yoke having not been eliminated when plotting

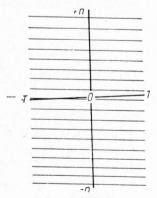

Fig. 32

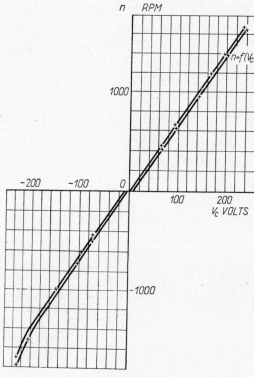

Fig. 33

the curve. The small step at $n = 0$ is due to the influence of the no-load torque of the motor and to the voltage drop across the brushes,

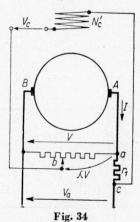

Fig. 34

This step may be essentially diminished, practically even to zero, by taking the feedback of the control winding from the internal voltage (or emf) of the motor to be controlled and not from the autodyne terminal voltage V (see below, in *Fig. 34*).

The quantity Π_1 which is compared with quantity Π_2 can represent the algebraic sum of any quantities Π_1' and Π_1'', etc. Thus, when feeding a motor through an autodyne, it is possible to control the quantity $V - K_3I$, where K_3 is a constant, instead of maintaining the terminal voltage V of the autodyne constant. Consequently, the slope of the straight lines diminishes *(Fig. 32)*.

For this purpose, winding N_c' has to be connected between points b and c *(Fig. 34)*. If the ratio of the voltage acting across points a and b to voltage V is λ, and the resistance connected through points a and c is r_1, the control law will be

$$\lambda V - Ir_1 = V_c \qquad\qquad (23)$$

i. e. the voltage V_a of the autodyne will be

$$V_a = V - Ir_1 = \frac{V_c}{\lambda} + Ir_1\frac{1-\lambda}{\lambda} \qquad\qquad (24)$$

This enables us to formulate a law according to which $V_a - K_3 I$ is constant, where

$$K_3 = \frac{r_1}{\lambda}(1-\lambda) \qquad\qquad (25)$$

The constant K_3 may easily be altered by the adequate choice of the ratio λ, in consequence of which the deviation of the motor speed from the constant one can be diminished accordingly.

It is clear that the law $\Pi_1 = \Pi_2$ can be formulated for any quantity capable of being expressed or measured electrically, even if it has no direct relation to the autodyne.

If, for instance, winding N_c' *(Fig. 23)* is not supplied by the voltage difference $V_c - V$, but by a voltage proportionate to the deviation of the motor speed from the constant one, the autodyne will keep the motor speed constant. Should the voltage feeding the winding N_c' be proportional to the difference between voltage V_c and the voltage V_G of a d-c generator G *(Fig. 35)*, then the autodyne, A operating as an exciter, will control the field current of the generator independently of load or speed in such a way as to achieve $V_G = V_c$. Relying on the same principle, the auto-

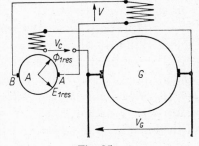

Fig. 35

dyne as an exciter is capable of controlling the current of generators or the speed, the power or the power factor, etc. of the motors.

In this way, the autodyne can work not only as a power con-
verter acting upon its own quantities and operation conditions, but also
as an automatic regulator of other machines or machine groups, and has
the advantage, over other automatically controlled exciters, of requiring
neither a separate driving motor, nor to be mounted on the shaft of the

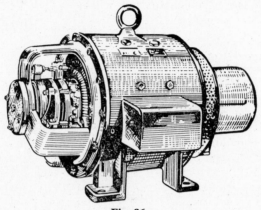

Fig. 36

machine to be controlled. In addition, the following essential condition
has to be emphasized.

As already mentioned, the impulses $\pm \Delta F'$ have small values. The power needed to produce them is incomparably smaller than that needed for the excitation of the generator and is negligible in comparison to the power of the autodyne.

Hence the autodyne represents a new electrical rotary amplifier
needing no driving motor.

In cases where the control power is of slight importance, $\pm \Delta F'$ can be obtained by two mmf's directed one against the other.

As an example of such a machine, we refer to an autodyne which, according to *Fig. 18*, keeps its load current constant. The control coil N'_c may be used also in a connection ensuring the maintenance of V constant. Such a possibility is provided in the autodynes of the experimental series AZ 140/72.

The autodynes of the experimental series AZ 140/72 *(Fig. 36)* represent universal machines capable of maintaining on request either the output voltage or the load current at a constant value. They are designed for charging storage batteries, i. e. for functions fulfilled earlier by motor generators of the series AZD.

All autodynes of the series AZ 140/72 are four-pole open-type machines. On the armature they have two separate windings (one for alternating current and one for direct current).

The main dimensions of the autodyne type AZ 140/72 are contained in *Table 1* referring to the machine represented in *Fig. 37*.

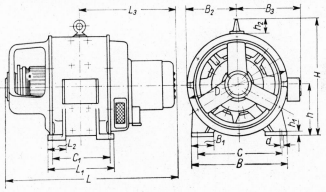

Fig. 37

TABLE 1

Type	Dimensions in mm															
	L	L_1	L_2	L_3	C	C_1	B	B_1	B_2	B_3	H	h	h_1	h_2	D	d
AZ –140/72	900	380	100	500	400	320	460	100	318	232	561	250	25	80	464	22

The technical data of the experimental series of the autodyne type AZ—140/72 are contained in *Table 2*.

TABLE 2

Rated three-phase line to line voltage	Rated a-c current	Rated power	Rated d-c current	Limits of d-c voltage variations	Rpm
V	A	kW	A	V	
380	24	10	140	45—72	1500

The control winding in the machines of type AZ—140/72 is supplied from the a-c mains by a transformer and a dry-plate rectifier, mounted together with the rheostats in a separate casing.

5*

Depending on the connection of the individual windings, the machines of type AZ—140/72 control the output current or voltage on the d-c side. They may be used in the following connections *(Fig. 38)*:

1. By disconnecting the load L, closing switch K_3 and turning the change-over switch K_2 into the left-side position, the circuit

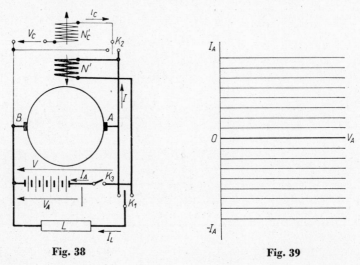

Fig. 38   Fig. 39

diagram of *Fig. 18* is realized. Winding N_c' carries a current i_c proportionate to voltage V_c. Thus the accumulator is charged by current I_A having a constant value, although the voltage V_A increases during charging. The current remains constant, even if the battery is short-circuited. This may be made clear by the following explanation: a steady-state operation can only be ensured if $\pm\Delta F' = 0$, i. e. if the above-mentioned mmf's are equal in magnitude and opposite to each other. In this case

$$I_A = i_c \frac{N_c'}{N'} \tag{26}$$

where N' is the number of turns of the winding carrying current I. If I_A deviates from this value, mmf impulses $\pm\Delta F'$ are created according to the above. By varying the current i_c, any desired value can be imparted to the charging current I_A *(Fig. 39)*. What is more: *by changing the direction of i_c I_A also changes its direction, the discharging of the battery begins and energy is being fed back through the autodyne*

*into the a-c mains. In this way storage batteries can be formed with
high efficiency.*

2. When switch K_1 is in its right-side position, a part I_L
of the current I of the autodyne passes through the load L. In this
case, for the above-mentioned reason, the autodyne keeps the current
constant:

$$I = I_A + I_L \tag{27}$$

If $I_L \leq I$, the battery is charged by I_A. If $I_L > I$, the
battery is discharged and an additional current is supplied to load L.

3. When switch K_1 is in its left-side position and switch K_2
in mid-position, the machine governs the voltage at $I = 0$ and the
voltage drop in winding N' is therefore negligible. Considering that
in the given case $I_A = I = 0$, it can be assumed in practice that

$$V = V_A \tag{28}$$

Therefore the autodyne, when working parallel with a buffer
battery, will maintain the voltage at the terminals of the load, strictly
on the level of battery voltage (or of another source connected parallel
to the autodyne).

4. When switch K_3 is disconnected, switch K_1 is in its left-
side position, and switch K_2 in the right-side position, a circuit diagram similar to that of *Fig. 23* is ob-
tained in which the load is fed by a
stabilized supply voltage, i. e.

$$V = V_c \tag{29}$$

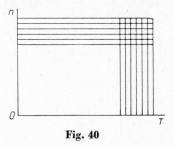

Fig. 40

The experimental machines,
referred to here, proved that the current I_A, even in case of an instantaneous short circuit, could steadily be
maintained constant.

If the battery is replaced by a separately excited d-c
motor, the latter will have an excavator characteristic *(Fig. 40)*,
because with currents smaller than $i_c N'_c/N'$ the autodyne works like
an ordinary rotary converter, i. e. $V \cong V_{max}$, consequently the speed
of the motor will be $n \cong$ constant. By increasing the current I to the
above-mentioned limit, the converter becomes an autodyne operating
according to characteristic $I =$ constant and therefore also $T =$ con-

stant. The desired stabilized speed n may be achieved by adjusting the field current of the motor, that of the stabilized torque T by changing the current i_c in the control coil of the autodyne.

The connection can be used expecially effectively as shown in *Fig. 41*. In this case a number of d-c motors are connected in

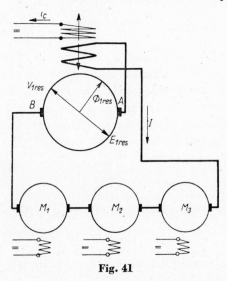

Fig. 41

series, receiving from an autodyne the current adjustable to any desired value. The torques of the motors can be set by the individual field coils.

In an instance dealt with above, the quantity Π_1 represents the algebraic sum of several quantities. Relying on the same principle, in *Figs. 16* and *18*, current i_c can be established by a voltage representing the difference between a controllable reference voltage V_c and the actual voltage λV, prevailing between points a and b of the potentiometer-connected rheostat *(Fig. 42a)*. In this way we have

$$i_c = \frac{V_c - \lambda V}{r'_c} \tag{30a}$$

where r'_c is the resistance of winding N'_c. The characteristic of the autodyne corresponds to the equation

$$I = \frac{V_c - \lambda V}{r'_c N'} N'_c \tag{30b}$$

Fig. 42b shows the characteristics 1, 2, 3, 4, 5 differing from each other by the value of λ and the characteristics 1', 2', 3', 4', 5' differing from the characteristics 1, 2, 3, 4, 5 by the value of V_c.

The quantity Π_2 representing the reference value for Π_1, has so far been chosen constant and independent of the operation conditions of the autodyne.

In principle, however, Π_2 itself may be a variable quantity. For instance, the quantity Π_2 may be understood to mean the mmf, proportional to the induced voltage E', of the winding connected

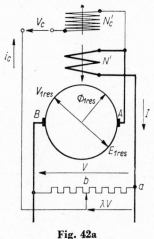

Fig. 42a   **Fig. 42b**

across the auxiliary brushes C and D, situated in the direct axis *(Fig. 43)*.

According to Eqs. (4), (5), (19) and (7) we obtain

$$E' = \sqrt{E_{max}^2 - E^2} \simeq V' \simeq \sqrt{V_{max}^2 - V^2} \tag{31}$$

i. e. the characteristic $V' = f(V)$ of the autodyne described here is a circle.

As the mmf of the winding supplied by the brushes C and D *(Fig. 43)* is proportional to E', and the mmf of the series winding has to equal the former in magnitude, the load curve can be expressed as

$$I \equiv \sqrt{V_{max}^2 - V^2} \tag{32}$$

i. e. by the equation of an ellipse in which the scale of the ordinate axis depends upon the constant of proportionality *(Fig. 44)*.

Fig. 45 shows test results of the experimental machine MITE proving the correctness of Eq. (31). As according to Eq. (10) $V_{max} = c_1 V_{1res}$, the radius of the circle is proportionate to the voltage of the a-c mains.

When this autodyne supplies a separately excited d-c motor, an excavator characteristic is obtained, whereby the torque *(Fig. 46)* can be varied according to *Fig. 44* by controlling current I.

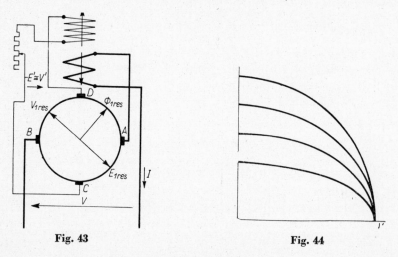

Fig. 43   Fig. 44

The speed n of the motor is regulated by varying its field current.

In this case the generated voltage E' feeds one of the control windings. At the same time, E' can also be used for acting upon another equipment connected with the autodyne, whereby the shape

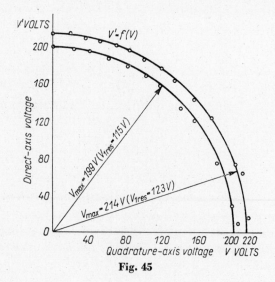

Fig. 45

of the desired characteristic can be changed within an even wider range.

As an example we refer to *Fig. 47*, in which the field coil of the motor M is fed by the voltage $V' + V_c$, where V_c is a given reference voltage and V' the voltage taken from the brushes C and D of the autodyne.

In this case, with small values of n, i. e. also with small V values, when $\cos \beta \cong 1$ and therefore $V' \cong V'_{max} \cong \cong V_{max} =$ constant, the initial part of the mechanical characteristic remains nearly parallel to the ordinate axis; consequently, it will be maintained as in *Fig. 46* with small values of n at $T =$ constant.

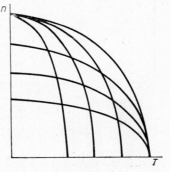

Fig. 46

When voltage V increases and V' decreases, the field current of the motor decreases too, i. e. the ratio of torque T to current I diminishes and the ratio of speed to voltage V increases. Hence the mechanical characteristic passes gradually into a curve following incidentally the law

$$T \equiv \frac{1}{n} \text{ i. e. } P = \text{constant}$$

When voltage V approaches V_{max}, it will be practically constant, while voltage V' decreases until zero, and the main flux in the motor is produced by voltage V_c only. In this way the characteristic assumes the form according to Eq. $n \cong$ constant *(Fig. 48)*.

There are many examples to show how the form of the characteristics and properties of the autodyne can sometimes be changed essentially by small alterations of the connections and interdependences.

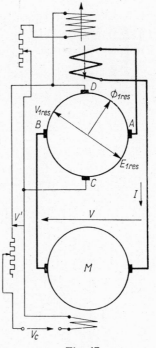

Fig. 47

It has been mentioned above that, in certain fields of application of the autodyne, not only the current of brushes A and B but also that of brushes C and D can be the load current. Since the voltage between the quadrature-axis brushes A and B is proportional to $\cos \beta$ and the voltage between the direct-axis brushes C and D is proportional to $\sin \beta$, these voltages, when supplying resistive loads, create the load current

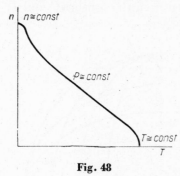

Fig. 48

$$I_L \equiv \cos \beta \qquad (33)$$

through the quadrature-axis brushes, and the load current

$$I'_L \equiv \sin \beta \qquad (34)$$

through the direct-axis brushes.

An example for the use of these currents is shown in *Fig. 49.*

Here the resistances are represented by the direct-axis and quadrature-axis coils of the generalized rotary converter RC, fed by the small auxiliary autodyne AA through brushes $A - B$ and $C - D$, respectively. In this way the currents I'_e and I_e shown in *Fig. 2a* are replaced by currents I_L and I'_L. This yields

$$F'_e \equiv \cos \beta' \qquad (35)$$

and

$$F_e \equiv \sin \beta' \qquad (36)$$

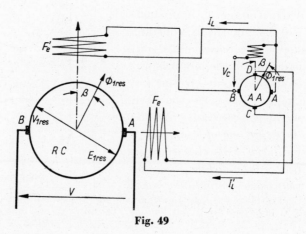

Fig. 49

The angle of the auxiliary autodyne is denoted here by β' in order to distinguish it from angle β of the converter.

By assuming the permeance of the direct axis and quadrature axis of the latter to be equal,

$$\cot \beta' = \frac{F'_e}{F_e} = \frac{\Phi'_1}{\Phi_1} \tag{37}$$

and by taking into consideration that according to Eqs. (1) and (2)

$$\frac{\Phi'_1}{\Phi_1} = \cot \beta \tag{38}$$

we obtain

$$\beta \simeq \beta' \tag{39}$$

In this way it will be obvious that the resulting flux in the generalized rotary converter automatically assumes almost the same position as the resulting flux in the auxiliary autodyne. This connection can be used whenever a continuous variation of voltage V within a positive and a negative limit is required. In such cases, the voltage V of the converter can be changed by varying the reference voltage V_c of the auxiliary autodyne.

The above examples show the autodyne when used for controlling certain quantities, as an auxiliary exciter supplying small exciting power to other machines (e. g. *Fig. 35*). The autodyne, however, can be used also as a booster which, while controlling certain quantities and co-operating with other machines, contributes to the power output of the whole machine set.

Figs. 50 and *51* show the schematic diagrams of an autodyne connected as a booster to another d-c source (marked by an oblong) having voltage V_D.

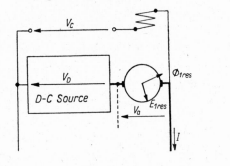

Fig. 50

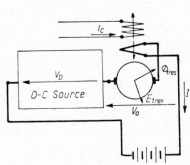

Fig. 51

Suppose, for instance, that voltage V_D varies within the limits $+V_{max}$ and $+V_{min}$, and the total voltage $V_a + V_D$ is to be stabilized at a reference value

$$V_c = \frac{+V_{max} + V_{min}}{2} \qquad (40)$$

In this case the autodyne can be designed for the voltage

$$V_a = \pm \frac{V_{max} - V_{min}}{2} \qquad (41)$$

to control according to

$$V_a + V_D = V_c \qquad (42)$$

When diminishing the voltage V_D until V_{min}, the autodyne adds a voltage

$$\frac{V_{max} - V_{min}}{2}$$

(Fig. 50), and when increasing V_D to V_{max}, the opposite voltage

$$-\frac{V_{max} - V_{min}}{2}$$

is added. In this way the autodyne can be designed according to the ratio

$$(V_{max} - V_{min}) : (V_{max} + V_{min})$$

for a power less than that of the whole machine set.

When, on the contrary, a voltage is required to vary within a wide range and V_D cannot be controlled correspondingly, the autodyne produces a voltage in the same direction as V_D or opposite to it, having a value at which the total voltage changes with the variation of control voltage V_c, according to Eq. (42).

In the next connection *(Fig. 51)* the autodyne maintains the current (e. g. of a battery) constant by the adequate automatic variation of V_a, which either coincides with, or is opposed to, the direction of V_D.

Fig. 52 shows a diagram of connection in which the autodyne adds not a voltage, but a current I_a to current I_D of the d-c source,

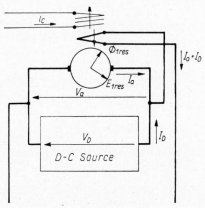

Fig. 52

controlling the total current according to

$$I_a + I_D = \text{constant}$$

There are quite a number of examples in which the autodyne not only controls definite quantities, but contributes to the power generation of the whole machine set.

CHAPTER 9

AUTODYNES WITH TWO-AXIS CONTROL

The connections of the autodyne enumerated in *Chapter 8* represent only a few particular cases of the many possible applications, resulting from the control windings being arranged not along one axis (either direct or quadrature) but along two axes.

Obviously, the number of such connections of practical importance is very great. Therefore we confine ourselves in this chapter to the treatment of a single problem: how to develop, according to the above principle, an autodyne which controls the load current in conformity with definite desired characteristics of different shapes.

Let us investigate first the basic diagram of *Fig. 53*, in which two windings are arranged, carrying the d-c control current i_c. One of the windings, with N_c' number of turns, is arranged in the direct axis, and the other, with N_c number of turns, along the quadrature axis. The load current I flows in a winding with N' number of turns, arranged along the direct axis and in another winding having N number of turns and acting in the quadrature axis.

The total mmf $\Sigma F'$, acting upward along the direct axis, produces, as it follows from the above investigations, the generator power $-3E_{1\text{res}}c_2\Sigma F' \sin\beta$ and a corresponding braking torque. Obviously, the total mmf ΣF acting in the quadrature axis produces, when directed from brush B toward brush A, a motor power $3E_{1\text{res}}c_2\Sigma F \cos\beta$, and a corresponding accelerating torque. Assuming no internal torque to be present, whereby the sum of the two powers mentioned above have to be zero, we obtain

$$\Sigma F' \sin\beta = \Sigma F \cos\beta \qquad (43a)$$

By taking into consideration that according to Eqs. (3), (7), (19) and (31)

$$\cos \beta = -\frac{E}{c_1 \, E_{1res}} \simeq \frac{V}{c_1 \, V_{1res}} \qquad (44a)$$

and

$$\sin \beta = \frac{E'}{c_1 \, E_{1res}} \simeq \frac{\sqrt{V_{max}^2 - V^2}}{c_1 \, V_{1res}} \qquad (44b)$$

we have the basic formula valid for all autodynes with two-axis control

$$\Sigma F' \cdot \sqrt{V_{max}^2 - V^2} = \Sigma F \cdot V \qquad (43b)$$

According to the circuit diagram of *Fig. 53,* the following equations are valid:

$$\Sigma F' = + i_c \, N_c' - I N' \qquad (45a)$$

and

$$\Sigma F = - i_c \, N_c + I N \qquad (45b)$$

Thus, by substituting (45a) and (45b) into (43a) and considering (44a) and (44b), we obtain for I the following formula, determining the load characteristic for the machine of *Fig. 53*:

$$I = i_c \, \frac{+ N_c \cos \beta + N_c' \sin \beta}{+ N \cos \beta + N' \sin \beta} =$$

$$= i_c \, \frac{+ N_c \, V + N_c' \sqrt{V_{max}^2 - V^2}}{+ N \, V + N' \sqrt{V_{max}^2 - V^2}} \qquad (46)$$

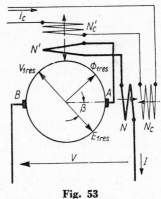

Fig. 53

It follows from Eq. (46) that, by the adequate choice of the number of turns of the individual windings and the directions of currents,* the most different shapes of characteristics may be obtained. The following examples should be mentioned:

* In Eq. (46) N_c, N_c', N, and N' have the positive sign when the mmfs belonging to them have the direction shown in *Fig. 53*. By reversing one or more of the windings in a way that their mmf's change their direction, the quantities concerned have to be taken with the negative sign.

1. By choosing the ratio $N_c/N_c' = N/N'$, with the mmf's having the direction shown in *Fig. 53*, the following equation is obtained:

$$I = i_c \frac{N_c'}{N'} \frac{\dfrac{N_c}{N_c'} \cos \beta + \sin \beta}{\dfrac{N}{N'} \cos \beta + \sin \beta} \qquad (47)$$

By excluding the case in which

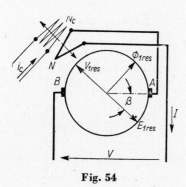

Fig. 54

$$\cos \beta + \frac{N_c'}{N_c} \sin \beta = 0$$

we arrive at

$$I = i_c \frac{N_c'}{N'} \qquad (48)$$

In this case the same characteristic is obtained as for the circuit diagram of *Fig. 16*, with the essential difference that the current is stabilized even when β approaches zero, because the limit value is conditioned by $-\tan \beta = N_c/N_c' = N/N'$ and not by $\beta = 0$.

This condition may have practical importance, whenever a small deviation from the ideal law of automatic control is only allowed to occur within the whole range $0° < \beta < 90°$.

The case of $N = N'$ and $N_c = N_c'$ may be of special interest. It can readily be understood that in this case the mmf's $i_c N_c'$ and $i_c N_c$ *(Fig. 53)* can be substituted by $i_c N_c$ *(Fig. 54)* equalling the geometrical sum of the former two and having a diagonal direction, while the mmf's IN' and IN can be substituted by the mmf IN equalling the geometrical sum of the two and arranged along the same diagonal, but acting opposite to $i_c N_c$.

An experimental machine and some AZ—140/72 type machines have been built in the MITE, according to *Fig. 54*.

2. Suppose now that $N = 0$-and $N_c \ll N'_c$ *(Fig. 55a)*. By altering the direction of the mmf of winding N_c according to *Fig. 55a* (i. e. N_c becomes negative), the Eqs. (44a) and (44b) yield

$$I = i_c \frac{N'_c \sin\beta - N_c \cos\beta}{N' \sin\beta} = i_c \left(\frac{N'_c}{N'} - \frac{N_c V}{N' \sqrt{V^2_{max} - V^2}} \right) \qquad (49)$$

The characteristics resulting from these formulas with different values of N'_c/N' are shown in *Fig. 55b*.

3. Suppose now that $N_c = 0$ and $N = N'$. Then, similarly to the former, the diagram of *Fig. 56a* is produced, and by the ade-

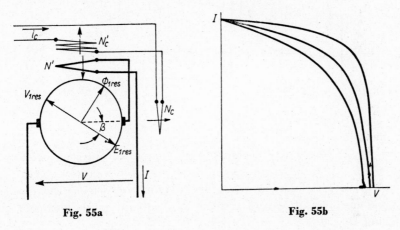

Fig. 55a   Fig. 55b

quate choice of the direction of mmf's, we arrive at the following formula

$$I = i_c \frac{N'_c}{N'} \frac{\sin\beta}{\sin\beta + \cos\beta} = i_c \frac{N'_c}{N'} \frac{\sqrt{V^2_{max} - V^2}}{\sqrt{V^2_{max} - V^2} + V} \qquad (50)$$

The corresponding current—voltage characteristic $I = f(V)$ is shown in *Fig. 56b*. It is not possible within the limits of this book to analyse all imaginable combinations of the connections in *Fig. 53*, resulting from imparting to the mmf's different directions and from assuming different possible ratios between the number of turns of the individual windings.

Nevertheless, we shall investigate one more possibility of further developing the circuit diagram of the autodyne described above.

Similarly to *Fig. 16*, which could be developed into *Figs. 23* and *26*, *Fig. 53* may also yield further diagrams in which the autodyne stabilizes not the current I but the voltage V. From the great number of these diagrams, we refer only to two *(Figs. 57a and 57b)* that may be developed like *Fig. 54* and serve for stabilizing the voltage V. The load characteristic $V = f(I)$ of an experimental machine, built by

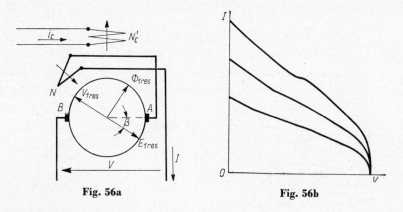

Fig. 56a   Fig. 56b

MITE according to this diagram, is represented in *Fig. 27* by curve I a line almost parallel to the abscissa.

With regard to other connections of the autodyne with two-axis control, we shall restrict ourselves — for want of space — to analyse, in the following chapters, diagrams featuring the problem of the accuracy of control and the most advantageous means of producing flux Φ_{1res}.

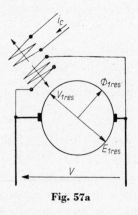

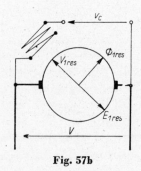

Fig. 57a   Fig. 57b

CHAPTER 10

THE INFLUENCE OF MAGNETIC CONFIGURATION UPON THE POSITION OF FLUX Φ_{1res}

In order to clarify the conditions ensuring an adequate degree of accuracy in control, it seems necessary to investigate the influence of some hitherto neglected factors likely to provoke certain deviations from the law of control.

One of these factors is, in the first place, the distribution of permeance in the machines along the different axes.

As it is known, an arbitrary system of mmf's, capable of rotating around a definite axis, seeks to assume a position in which the flux produced by it and the permeance attain their maximum. When permeance varies with the direction of the mmf, a reluctance torque, well known from the theory of machines, arises tending to rotate the mmf system to a position, in which the permeance is the greatest.

It is clear that the same phenomenon will arise also in the autodyne, when the permeance of the machine varies in the different directions the flux Φ_{1res} may assume.

If we presume meanwhile that the magnetic saturation of iron can be neglected, the problem of permeance is limited to the character of geometrical configuration of the magnetic circuit.

The magnetic circuit of the autodyne can have two basic forms.

1. The machine may have undivided poles *(Fig. 58a)*, or poles split into two halves sufficiently near to each other practically not to change the permeance for the direct-axis flux in spite of the two parts *(Fig. 58b)*.

2. The machine may have split poles arranged diagonally, yielding a magnetic circuit for a two-pole autodyne like the one of a four-pole d-c machine *(Fig. 59)*.

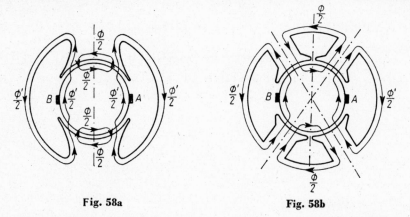

Fig. 58a   Fig. 58b

     As all autodynes built so far have been constructed according to the principle described in point 2 *(Fig. 59)*, we shall investigate this case first.

     Since the machine has only four symmetry planes and its permeance is not uniform in all directions, as has so far been supposed,

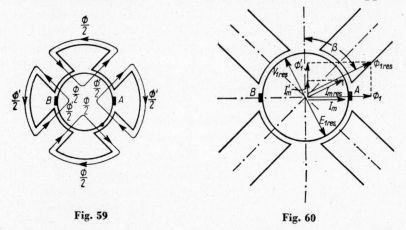

Fig. 59   Fig. 60

one would be tempted, at first sight, to think that in such an autodyne a reluctance torque should arise.

     A more thorough investigation will, however, show that no such danger is to be feared.

     Divide the magnetizing current $\overline{I_{mres}}$ *(Fig. 60)* into two components, one of which $\overline{I'_m}$ acts in the direct axis and the other $\overline{I_m}$ in the quadrature axis of the machine. The ratio of flux Φ', produced by the mmf of current I'_m *(Fig. 59)* to current I'_m, determines the permeance (or more precisely the permeance multiplied by the number of turns) of the machine along the direct axis. It is obviously equal to that along the quadrature axis, determined by the ratio of flux Φ to the current I_m by the mmf of which Φ is provoked. Therefore

$$\frac{I_m}{\Phi} = \frac{I'_m}{\Phi'} = c_3 \tag{51}$$

On the other hand

$$\frac{\Phi}{\Phi_1} = \frac{\Phi'}{\Phi'_1} = c_4 \tag{52}$$

where c_3 and c_4 are constants.

Therefore according to Eqs. (1), (2), (51) and (52)

$$\frac{I_m}{I'_m} = \frac{\Phi_1}{\Phi'_1} = \tan \beta \tag{53}$$

It follows therefrom, as shown in *Fig. 60*, that the vector of current $\overline{I_{mr\ s}}$ at any arbitrary angle β coincides in direction with vector $\overline{\Phi_{1r\ s}}$. i. e. is perpendicular to vector $\overline{E_{1r\ s}}$, and therefore has no active component, without which no reluctance torque can arise.

Though in this case the magnetic configuration is different in different directions, this circumstance in the autodyne of Fig. 59 does not appear to influence the above results and to impair the accuracy of stabilization.

Now we shall investigate the constructional features of the autodyne built according to *Fig. 58*. In this case the permeances along the direct and quadrature axes are not equal. Hence the coefficients referring to one axis will be different from those referring to the other axis. Let us use the notation of coefficients adopted so far for denoting the relations between quantities bearing no "comma" and choose c'_1, c'_2, c'_3, c'_4 for denoting the coefficients characterizing the relations between quantities marked by "comma".

In this configuration the fluxes Φ_{max} and Φ_{1max} (arising when $\beta = 90°$) can be produced only by a current $I_{m max}$ obviously greater than current $I'_{m max}$, necessary for producing the fluxes Φ'_{max} and Φ'_{1max}, arising when $\beta = 0$. From Eqs. (51) and (52) it follows that

$$I_{m max} = c_3 c_4 \Phi_{1max} \tag{54}$$

and, accordingly,

$$I'_{m\max} = c'_3\, c'_4\, \Phi'_{1\max} \tag{55}$$

Taking into consideration that according to Eqs. (1) and (2)

$$\Phi_{1\max} = \Phi'_{1\max} \tag{56}$$

it follows for the configuration given here that

$$c_3\, c_4 > c'_3\, c'_4 \tag{57}$$

The motor power of current I'_m is

$$3\, c'_3\, c'_4\, E_{1res}\, \Phi'_{1res} \sin \beta$$

The generator power of current I_m is

$$-\,3\, c_3\, c_4\, E_{1res}\, \Phi_1 \cos \beta$$

By considering Eqs. (1) and (2) and also the fact that at a given frequency

$$\frac{E_{1res}}{\Phi_{1res}} = c_5 \tag{58}$$

where c_5 is a constant, we arrive at the result that the algebraic sum of these powers, i. e. the active power P_{mres} produced by the current I_{mres} is

$$P_{mres} = -\,\frac{3\, E^2_{1res}}{2\, c_5}\, (c_3\, c_4 - c'_3\, c'_4)\, \sin 2\beta \tag{59}$$

Since this expression has a negative sign, electric power is generated involving braking reluctance torque

$$T_r = \frac{P_{mres}}{\omega} \tag{60}$$

where ω is the angular velocity.

It becomes evident that in the machine, with the configuration mentioned in *Fig. 58b*, a reluctance torque T_r proportional to $\sin 2\beta$ arises endeavouring to rotate the magnetic flux toward the direct axis. It has a maximum value at $\beta = 45°$, $\beta = 135°$, $\beta = 225°$ and $\beta = 315°$, and disappears at $\beta = 0°$, $\beta = 90°$, $\beta = 180°$, and $\beta = 270°$.

According to Eqs. (59) and (60)

$$T_r \equiv c_3\, c_4 - c'_3\, c'_4 \tag{61}$$

Certainly, this reluctance torque can easily be eliminated. It is sufficient to add to the stator a coil fed from the brushes A and B, i. e. by the emf E and lying along the direct axis. Here the mmf produced by the coil is of the magnitude $c_6 E$ (where c_6 is a constant) and has the direction shown in *Fig. 61*.

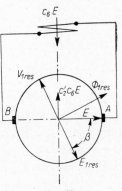

Fig. 61

In this case the compensating current $c_2' c_6 E$, provoked by this mmf and directed upwards, will produce the motor power

$$3 E_{1\mathrm{r\,s}}\, c_2'\, c_6\, E \sin \beta = \frac{3 E_{1\mathrm{res}}^2\, c_1\, c_2'\, c_6}{2} \sin 2\beta$$

(see Eqs. 6 and 8).

By choosing

$$c_1\, c_2'\, c_3 = \frac{c_3\, c_4 - c_3'\, c_4'}{c_5} \qquad (62)$$

the total power of currents $I_{mr\,s}$ and $c_2' c_6 E$ will equal zero, i. e. the reluctance torque due to the magnetic configuration represented in *Fig. 58a* and *58b** will be completely eliminated at any angle β by the coil shown in *Fig. 61*.

---

* In *Chapter 17* such diagrams of connections will be shown as practically exclude the detrimental effects of the reluctance torque and the problem of their elimination.

THE INFLUENCE OF MAGNETIC SATURATION
UPON THE POSITION OF FLUX Φ_{1res}

An advantageous exploitation of the autodyne can be achieved — as in other machines — by admitting a certain degree of saturation. Let us investigate how the saturation affects the accuracy of control.

We have so far assumed the ratios I_m/Φ_1 and I'_m/Φ'_1 as being expressed by constant quantities $c_3 c_4$ and $c'_3 c'_4$, resp., independent of the magnitudes of fluxes and currents. Nevertheless, the field current in a d-c generator, necessary, e. g., for producing increasing load currents, grows rather than the flux Φ'.

On investigating the ratio of magnetizing current to the magnetic flux in the autodyne, we find the ratios I_m/Φ_1 and I'_m/Φ'_1 to remain practically constant at the variation of quantities Φ_1 and Φ'_1 caused, by the variation of the position of flux Φ_{1res}.

For the investigation of this very complicated problem — so far as it is possible within the limits of this book — we shall start from the assumption of a uniformly distributed air gap.

Let us first assume (*Fig. 62a*) that $\beta = 0$, $\Phi_1 = 0$, and $\Phi'_1 = \Phi'_{1max} = \Phi_{1r\,s}$ and that the quantity I'_{mmax}/Φ'_{1max} is chosen with regard to magnetic saturation.

Suppose now that Φ_{1res} reaches the position shown in *Fig. 62b*. As the air gap is everywhere of the same magnitude, the value of the mmf necessary for the flux to be driven through it remains unchanged. Obviously, the distribution of flux density inside the iron core, i. e. the saturation remains unchanged as well.

It follows that for producing the former quantity $\Phi_{1r\,s}$ the current $I_{mr\,s}$ must have the value as before, i. e.

$$I_{mres} = I'_{mmax}$$

and that the ratio I_{mres}/Φ_{1res} has, for any angle β, the constant value $c_3 c_4$.

On the other hand, the current vector $\overline{I_{mres}}$ will always coincide in its direction with vector $\pmb{\Phi}_{1r\ s}$. Therefore the direct-axis component of current $I_{mr\ s}$ will be

$$I'_m = I_{mres} \cos \beta \qquad (63)$$

and the quadrature-axis component

$$I_m = I_{mres} \sin \beta \qquad (64)$$

By taking into consideration that the fluxes $\pmb{\Phi}'_1$ and $\pmb{\Phi}^1$ equal, as before, $\pmb{\Phi}_{1r\ s} \cos \beta$ and $\pmb{\Phi}_{1r\ s} \sin \beta$, respectively, we have

and

$$\left. \begin{aligned} \frac{I'_m}{\Phi'_1} &= \frac{I_{mres}}{\Phi_{1res}} = c_3 c_4 \\[2mm] \frac{I_m}{\Phi_1} &= \frac{I_{mres}}{\Phi_{1res}} = c_3 c_4 \end{aligned} \right\} \qquad (65)$$

i. e. all results obtained while neglecting saturation remain valid.

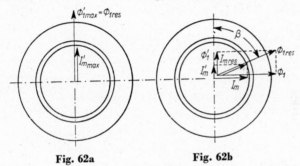

Fig. 62a   Fig. 62b

The fact that the ratios Φ_1/I_m and Φ'_1/I'_m are constant in the investigated autodyne, while in a d-c generator the permeance of the magnetic circuit varies strongly with saturation, can be explained physically in the following way.

In the generator the diminishing of flux means an actual diminishing of flux density in the whole magnetic circuit and a corresponding diminution of saturation. In the autodyne, however, flux Φ is simultaneously increased by diminishing flux Φ' and the degree of saturation is determined by the interplay of these two fluxes. In this way the saturation for fluxes Φ' and Φ remains unchanged.

The problem becomes more involved when investigating it for the case of the configuration shown in *Fig. 59*, because now the distribution of flux density inside the iron core will be different for different values of angle β, owing to the unequal length of the air gap. Nevertheless, it can easily be demonstrated that in this case also, whenever — on account of the saturation varying with different values of angle β — a certain reluctance torque arises, this will have an insignificant value.

A reluctance torque can only arise when current $\overline{I_{mres}}$ has an active component. If, however, flux $\overline{\Phi_{1res}}$ assumes one of those

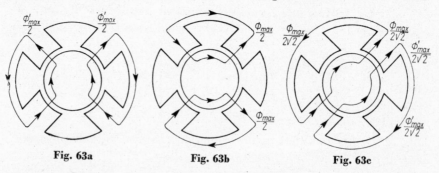

Fig. 63a   Fig. 63b   Fig. 63c

positions, in which its direction coincides with one of the symmetry axes, (direct axis, quadrature axis and the two diagonal ones), the direction of current $\overline{I_{mres}}$ and of flux $\overline{\Phi_{1res}}$ are bound to coincide because of the symmetry of the system and, consequently, no reluctance torque can arise.

Assuming, however, the permeance for the angles $\beta = 45°$ $\beta = 135°$, $\beta = 225°$ and $\beta = 315°$, i. e. in the direction of the diagonal axes, to be smaller or greater than for angles $\beta = 0°$, $\beta = 90°$, $\beta = 180°$, and $\beta = 270°$, i. e. in the direction of the direct and quadrature axes, then the magnet system, when in mid-position (as for instance, $\beta = 22.5°$, $\beta = 67.5°$, $\beta = 112.5°$, etc.), will try to rotate toward the axis in which the permeance is greater, and a reluctance torque will arise proportionate to about the value $\sin 4\beta$.

In addition, a condition of theoretical interest should be considered. It is evidently easy to choose the characteristics of the magnetic circuit in such a manner that the amount of magnetic saturation be practically the same, in case $\overline{\Phi_{1r\,s}}$ adopts a diagonal position and in case it acts along the direct or quadrature axis.

Let us investigate first the cases when $\beta = 0$ *(Fig. 63a)* and $\beta = 90°$ *(Fig. 63b)*. In both cases half of the flux passes through each half pole and closes through the appropriate part of the stator and rotor yokes. When $\beta = 45°$, the direct-axis flux shown in *Fig. 63a* decreases to the value $\Phi'_{max} \cos 45°$, while the quadrature-axis flux increases to the value $\Phi_{max} \sin 45°$. In two half poles these fluxes are opposite to each other, while they are summed up in the other two. Hence, the actual flux is distributed as in *Fig. 63c*.

Hence the flux through the half poles is greater, than in the cases shown in *Figs. 63a* and *63b*, i. e. the flux density in the pole and in the teeth reaches a $\sqrt{2}$-time value, while the flux passing through the yokes of the stator and rotor reduces in the ratio $\sqrt{2} : 1$. Thus in the direct-axis or quadrature-axis position of flux Φ_{1res}, the increase of consumption in ampere turns along the yokes — if the quantities concerned are chosen adequately — compensates for the decrease of consumption in ampère turns of the teeth and of the pole. It follows that an autodyne, having the configuration of *Fig. 59*, can be built in such a way that the ratio I_{mres}/Φ_{1res} be practically the same for the diagonal position of flux $\overline{\Phi_{1res}}$, as for its direct-axis or quadrature-axis position. Hence the reluctance torque disappears also for the mid-positions

$$\beta = \ \ 22.5° \ \ (Fig. 64),$$
$$\beta = \ \ 67.5°,$$
$$\beta = 112.5°, \text{ etc.}$$

For the configuration shown in *Fig. 58*, the problem of flux distribution becomes even more complicated if $\beta = 45°$. But also in this case it is clear that, when β approaches $45°$, the actual flux decreases in the two half poles, while it increases in the other two halves approximately by the ratio $\sqrt{2} : 1$. Thus the results obtained above remain essentially valid.

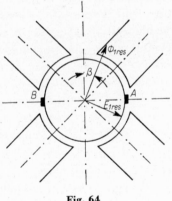

Fig. 64

In this way it may be expected that by using the coil shown in *Fig. 61* no reluctance torques will arise in this case either.*

---

* See footnote at the end of *Chapter 10*.

STATOR SLIP EXCITATION

In order to ensure the state of indifferent equilibrium for Φ_{1res}, we omitted the usual stator field coils of converters, because their mmf provokes, together with the armature, certain torques hampering the free displacement of the flux.

In order to eliminate these torques in the autodyne *(Figs. 11 and 20)*, a rotor excitation system has been produced, by which the exciting mmf, set up by the rotor current I_{mres}, turns together with Φ_{1res}, when the latter and the rotor slip. This *"rotor slip excitation"* has, however, many shortcomings in practice. The most essential of them is that the magnetizing current additionally loads the armature, and deteriorates thereby the power factor $\cos \varphi$, which would be highly objectionable in autodynes of medium and high capacity. Therefore the question arises whether the sole way of releasing the armature of the torque, acting upon it and provoked by the field coil, is to omit this winding, as has been done so far, or this aim may be achieved in another way without producing a rotor-exciting current.

This problem has been solved in the form of the "winding system of stator slip excitation", ensuring automatically the new distribution of stator mmf, required by the varying direction of flux Φ_{1res} without producing torque.

For the development of this system of stator windings, it is advisable to start from the phenomenon of compensating currents described above, i. e. to add to this exciting mmf, produced by rotor current I_{mres}, a stator mmf provoking in the rotor, at any arbitrary value of angle β, a compensating current equal and opposite to current I_{mres}.

Let us investigate this question for an autodyne with the configuration shown in *Fig. 59*. We start here from Eqs. (1), (2), (6), (7), (51), (52), and (58) yielding

$$I_m = c_3 c_4 \, \Phi_{1\text{res}} \sin \beta = \frac{c_3 c_4}{c_5} E_{1\text{res}} \sin \beta = \frac{c_3 c_4}{c_5} E_1' \qquad (66)$$

and

$$I_m' = c_3 c_4 \, \Phi_{1\text{res}} \cos \beta = \frac{c_3 c_4}{c_5} E_1 \qquad (67)$$

The problem is solved by producing, along the direct and quadrature axis, stator mmf's F_e' and F_e, respectively, making the compensating current provoked by F_e' equal I_m', and the other provoked by F_e, equal I_n. As in case of Eq. (11), the values of these mmf's should be

$$F_e' = \frac{I_m'}{c_2} = \frac{c_3 c_4}{c_5 c_2} E_1 \qquad (68)$$

and

$$F_e = \frac{I_m}{c_2} = \frac{c_3 c_4}{c_5 c_2} E_1' \qquad (69)$$

It follows that the problem of creating a system of windings for the stator slip excitation is solved, when current I_e' (*Fig. 2a*) is made proportional to E_1 and current I_e to E_1'.

By considering that, according to Eq. (8), $c_1 E_1 = E$, the current I_e', produced by the emf between brushes B and A, will be found sufficient for creating the necessary mmf F_e'.

In this case the mmf F_e' will be

$$F_e' = c_6' E = c_6' c_1 E_1 \qquad (70)$$

where c_6' is a constant differing from c_6.

By choosing the constants in a way that

$$c_6' c_1 = \frac{c_3 c_4}{c_5 c_2} \qquad (71)$$

the mmf F_e' ensures the suppression of current I_m' (Eq. 68).

At the position of flux $\overline{\Phi_{1\text{res}}}$, assumed in the diagram of time vectors (*Fig. 2b*), the emf E_1' lags behind E_1 by 90°. Hence, when the emf E_1 induced in the phase winding by Φ_1' corresponds to the emf on the d-c side $E = c_1 E_1$, acting along the axis of brushes B and A, then the emf E_1' on the d-c side corresponds to the emf $E' = c_1 E_1'$, acting along the axis perpendicular to the axis of brushes A and

B. By arranging along this axis the auxiliary brushes C and D, designed only for small exciting currents and feeding a winding that carries the current I_e, and has the same cross section and the same number of turns as the winding carrying current I'_e, the mmf produced in it will be

$$F_e = c'_6\, E' = c'_6\, c_1\, E'_1 = \frac{c_3\, c_4}{c_5\, c_2}\, E'_1 \qquad (72)$$

i. e. will have a value eliminating I_m (Eq. 69).

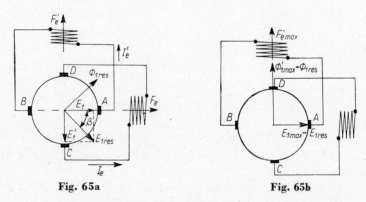

Fig. 65a   Fig. 65b

In this way, we obtain (Fig. 65a) the desired winding system for stator slip excitation, ensuring, at any arbitrary position of flux $\overline{\Phi_{1res}}$, the stator mmf necessary for producing the fluxes Φ' and Φ. The same diagram of connections for the case $\beta = 0°$ and $E_1 = E_{1max} = E_{1res}$ is shown in *Fig. 65b*. Here the internal voltage E, prevailing between the brushes B and, A has the value E_{max} and produces the mmf F'_{emax}. On the other hand, $E'_1 = 0$, $E' = 0$ and, therefore, the mmf $F'_e = 0$.

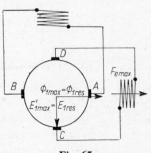

Fig. 65c

In this way the mmf acts along the direct axis only, corresponding to the position of $\overline{\Phi_{1res}}$. The maximum value F'_{emax} complies with the condition that Φ'_1 also reaches the maximum value $\Phi'_{1max} = \Phi_{1res}$.

Fig. 65c shows the altered distribution for the case $\beta = 90°$.

The addition of the stator winding system *(Fig. 65a)*, freeing completely the rotor from the magnetizing current, creates practically no torque. This may be shown by the following considerations.

The compensating current $c_2 F'_e$ influenced by the mmf F'_e, produces the generator power $-3 c_2 E_{1res} F'_e \sin \beta$ which, by considering Eqs. (68) and (6), is found to equal

$$- 3 \frac{c_3 c_4}{2 c_5} E^2_{1res} \sin 2\beta$$

The compensating current $c_2 F_e$, according to Eqs. (69) and (7), yields the motor power

$$3 c_2 E_{1res} F_e \cos \beta = 3 \frac{c_3 c_4}{2 c_5} E^2_{1res} \sin 2\beta$$

In this way the total power is zero, i. e. the adding of the winding system for stator slip excitation, represented in Fig. 65, provokes no torque and does not disturb — unlike the field coil of the converter — the state of indifferent equilibrium of flux $\overline{\Phi_{1res}}$.

These experimental autodynes built in the MITE were equipped with a winding system for slip excitation, according to *Fig. 65.*

Fig. 66 shows some test results of this machine. They prove the correctness of what has been said about the function of the winding system for slip excitation. As is to be seen, the autodyne operated for a period without these windings, and this caused the reactive component of line current $I_e \sin \varphi$, corresponding to current I_{mres}, to equal 8 A and the power factor $\cos \varphi$ to be low (0·3). After switching on these windings, the component $I_e \sin \varphi$ disappeared and the power factor $\cos \varphi$ was raised to unity.

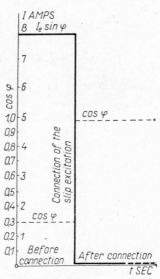

Fig. 66

The fact that the adding of the windings mentioned above does not provoke any additional torque and does not interfere with the control process, is corroborated by *Fig. 67*, showing the characteristic $V = f(V_c)$ obtained during the operation of the experimental machine of the MITE, built according to *Fig. 57b*. The points marked by a dark dot or a circle, indicating the presence or the absence of these exciting windings, respectively are found to lie along the same straight line.

Further investigations showed that the same result could be achieved more economically and simply with the diagram of *Fig. 68,* where only one auxiliary brush D is provided. The arrows along the

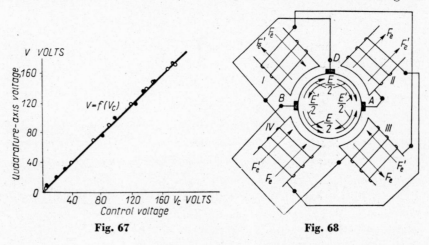

Fig. 67   Fig. 68

armature show the direction of the emf E'. Obviously, the internal voltage

$$\frac{E - E'}{2}$$

arises between brushes B and D and the voltage

$$\frac{E + E'}{2}$$

between brushes D and A. The former feeds the windings, on the half poles I and III, while the latter supplies the windings on the half poles II and IV.

By the adequate choice of certain quantities, the mmf of the windings fed from brushes B and D can be made equal to $c_6'(E - E')$ and the mmf of the windings fed from brushes D and A, equal to $c_6'(E + E')$. Eqs. (70) and (72) show that, in this case, the mmf of the windings on the half poles I and III will have the value $F_e' - F_e$*

---

* See first footnote in *Chapter 3.*

and the mmf of the windings on the half poles II and IV will have the value $F'_e + F_e$. The arrows in *Fig. 68* show the directions in which the individual parts F'_e and F_e of the total mmf are acting in each half pole.

The comparison of *Figs. 68* and *59* shows that the mmf's F'_e coincide in direction with flux Φ', and the mmf's F_e with flux Φ.

Thus it is clear that, by the adequate choice of c'_6, the winding system of *Fig. 68* can provoke mmf's subject to the same variation laws as the mmfs of the winding system in *Fig. 65*. At the same time the winding system of *Fig. 68* permits considerable savings in copper, as compared to the winding system of *Fig. 65*.

In *Fig. 65* both exciting windings have to be rated for mmf's $F_{emax} = F'_{emax}$ developing at $\beta = 0$ and $\beta = 90°$, i. e. when one of the windings carries no current.

On the other hand, in *Fig. 68*, the same windings produce the mmf F'_{emax} at $\beta = 0$, the mmf F_{emax} at $\beta = 90°$, and the mmf

$$c'_6 \frac{E_{max} + E'_{max}}{\sqrt{2}} = \frac{F'_{emax} + F_{emax}}{\sqrt{2}} = \sqrt{2}\, F_{emax}$$

at $\beta = 45°$, when the emf between the brushes D and A is

$$\frac{E_{max} + E'_{max}}{2\sqrt{2}}$$

It follows that, in *Fig. 65*, all half poles should be constructed with two windings, each of them rated for the mmf F_{emax}*, while in *Fig. 68* each half pole has but one winding rated for the mmf $\sqrt{2}\, F_{emax}$.

The experimental types AB and AZ were built according to *Fig. 68*.

Since it is highly important in the theory of the autodyne to know the influence the different torques have on the law of control, it will not be superfluous to prove that the windings, arranged as shown in *Fig. 68* cannot create any torque either.

To begin with, we shall determine the value of the compensating current, produced only by the mmf $F'_e + F_e$ of the half poles II and IV. The mmf $F'_e + F_e$ of each coil of these half poles can be

---

* It should be considered that the winding in the direct axis in *Fig. 65a*, when used according to *Fig. 59*, consists of four coils, each arranged on a half pole, producing the mmf F'_e (see also first footnote in *Chapter 3*) and creating together Φ'. The same applies to the quadrature axis.

represented by the sum of two mmf's

$$\frac{F'_e + F_e}{2}$$

Let us create on the half poles I and III two equal and opposite mmf's *(Fig. 69a)* :

$$\frac{F'_e + F_e}{2}$$

The adding of these mmf's has no influence on the distribution of magnetic flux. *Fig. 69a* shows that the mmf's obtained in this way form

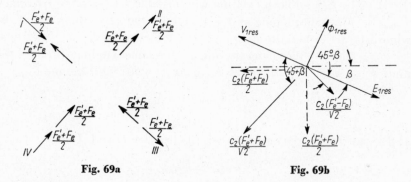

Fig. 69a   Fig. 69b

two systems, one of them acting in the direct axis of the machine, directed upwards (the arrows nearer to the center), the second acting along the quadrature axis, from left to right (the arrows farther away from the center). The mmf in each system has the value

$$\frac{F'_e + F_e}{2}$$

The first system provokes a compensating current

$$\frac{c_2(F'_e + F_e)}{2} \; *$$

---

* It may seem possible to find the total mmf, provoking the compensating current, by adding up the vectors represented in *Fig. 69a*. This, however, is not so because of the following considerations:

1. The arrows in *Fig. 69a* are not vectors, but only show the directions of the parts of the mmf quadrangularly distributed along the half poles.

2. The aggregate mmf is the sum of the mmf's created in each pole (see the first footnote in *Chapter 3* and the preceding one in this chapter).

directed downwards *(Fig. 69b)*. The second system creates a compensating current of the same value, but directed from right to left. The resulting current, obtained by the geometrical addition of the two currents mentioned above, denoted by dotted lines, represents the required compensating current, provoked only by the mmf's $F'_e + F_e$ of the half poles II and IV. This compensating current has the value

$$\frac{c_2(F'_e + F_e)}{\sqrt{2}}$$

and includes with vector $\overline{V_{1\text{res}}}$ an angle $\beta + 45°$. Consequently, it produces according to Eqs. (6), (7), (70), (71) and (72) the motor power

$$\frac{3\,c_2\,E_{1\text{res}}}{\sqrt{2}}(F_e + F'_e)\cos(45° + \beta) = \frac{3}{2}c_2\,E_{1\text{res}}(F_e + F'_e)(\cos\beta - \sin\beta) =$$

$$= \frac{3\,c_3\,c_4\,E_{1\text{res}}}{2\,c_5}(\cos\beta + \sin\beta)(\cos\beta - \sin\beta) = \frac{3\,c_3\,c_4\,E^2_{1\text{res}}}{2\,c_5}\cos 2\beta$$

Analogously, the compensating current provoked by the mmf of half poles I and III *(Fig. 68)* has the value

$$\frac{c_2(F'_e - F_e)}{\sqrt{2}}$$

(Fig. 69b) and includes with voltage $E_{1\text{res}}$ an angle $180° - (45° - \beta) =$ $= 135° + \beta$. Therefore, its generator power is

$$-\frac{3\,c_2\,E_{1\text{res}}}{\sqrt{2}}(F'_e - F_e)\cos(45° - \beta) =$$

$$= -\frac{3\,c_2\,E^2_{1\text{res}}}{2\,c_5}(\cos\beta - \sin\beta)(\cos\beta + \sin\beta) = -\frac{3\,c_3\,c_4\,E^2_{1\text{res}}}{2\,c_5}\cos 2\beta$$

Hence the algebraic sum of powers and, consequently, also the sum of torques produced by all the mmf's of the windings in the investigated system equal zero.

Let us investigate now the problem of developing a winding system for the stator slip excitation in an autodyne with the configuration of *Fig. 58b*. In this case the currents I'_m and I_m, according to Eqs. (66) and (67), will be equal:

$$I'_m = c'_3 c'_4 \Phi'_1 \tag{73}$$

and

$$I_m = c_3 c_4 \Phi_1 \tag{74}$$

respectively.

In order to diminish the current I'_m to zero, a stator mmf F'_e has to be produced, provoking a compensating current $c'_2 F'_e$ equal and opposite to I'_m, i. e. according to Eqs. (1), (6), (58) similarly to Eq. (8) we obtain

$$F'_e = \frac{c'_3 c'_4}{c'_2} \Phi'_1 = \frac{c'_3 c'_4}{c'_2 c_5} E_1 = \frac{c'_3 c'_4}{c'_1 c'_2 c_5} E \tag{75}$$

Similarly, we find that for diminishing I_m to zero, a stator mmf

$$F_e = \frac{c_3 c_4}{c_1 c_2 c_5} E' \tag{76}$$

is necessary.

Thus in the autodyne of *Fig. 58b*, the slip excitation can in principle be ensured by the winding system of *Fig. 65*, if the cross section of the winding acting along the direct axis and the corresponding mmf are diminished in the ratio

$$\frac{F_{e\max}}{F'_{e\max}} = \frac{c'_1 c'_2 c_3 c_4}{c_1 c_2 c'_3 c'_4}$$

The diagram of connections in *Fig. 68* can also be used for this purpose by adding the small coil, shown in *Fig. 61* and designed to diminish the mmf along the direct axis in the ratio

$$\frac{c'_1 c'_2 c_3 c_4}{c_1 c_2 c'_3 c'_4}$$

Should these windings be used for autodynes of *Fig. 58b*, great difficulties would arise in the commutation, because of the direct-axis brushes coming under the influence of the direct-axis flux Φ'.

There are, however, two expedients enabling us to omit the direct-axis brushes C and D, and thereby to use for these machines the configuration shown in *Fig. 58*. The first expedient can be used with autodynes of both low and high capacity, but only within certain fields of application. The second expedient can be used for any autodyne, though it is economical only for medium-capacity and high-capacity ones.

The first expedient is based on the following considerations:

$$E' = c_1 E_{1res} \sin \beta = E_{max} \sin \beta$$

and

$$E = c_1 E_{1res} \cos \beta = E_{max} \cos \beta$$

According to Eq. (31) the following relation is valid between these two quantities

$$E' = \sqrt{E_{max}^2 - E^2} \simeq V' \simeq \sqrt{V_{max}^2 - V^2}$$

This is the equation of a circle. *Fig. 70a* shows a quadrant valid for the positive values of V and V' (curve $1-2-3-4$).

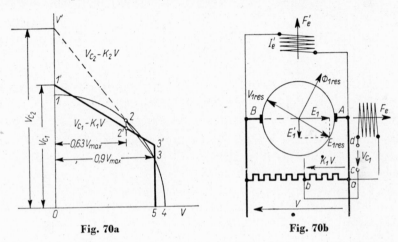

Fig. 70a   Fig. 70b

Suppose now that the autodyne has to control the voltage within the limits $0.9\, V_{max}$ (point 3) and zero. When V decreases within these limits, the voltage V' increases from the value $3-5$ to the value $1-0$. By substituting the part $1-2-3$ of the circle by a straight line $1'-2'-3'$, the maximum deviations in voltage will be relatively small (sections $1'-1$, $2-2'$, $3'-3$).

In other words, only a small error will be committed if the mmf F_e *(Fig. 70b)* is not produced by voltage $V' = \sqrt{V_{max}^2 - V^2}$ but by voltage equalling $V_{C1} - k_1 V$ and corresponding to the ordinates of the straight line $1'-2'-3'$. This can be achieved by feeding the exciting winding along the quadrature axis by the difference of two voltages. One of these voltages prevailing between points d and c is constant, and has the value V_{C1}. The second has the value $k_1 V$, and is taken from points a and b of the resistance connected in parallel to brushes A and B.

Thus we have obtained a voltage differing but slightly from V', to feed the quadrature-axis winding as in *Fig. 65*, although the additional brushes C and D are here omitted. The deviations from the ideal law of control, arising in this case, are so unimportant that, in many fields, where no great accuracy of control is required, they have no practical importance.

Fig. 70c shows two quadrants of the circle $V' = \sqrt{V_{max}^2 - V^2}$. The ordinates correspond to values of V' to be connected to the ter-

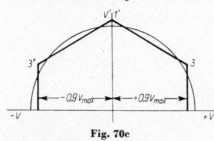

Fig. 70c

minals of the quadrature-axis exciting winding, in order to change V from a maximum positive value to a maximum negative value. In this case the winding can be fed without using brushes C and D, if the corresponding quadrant in the domain of negative V values is also substituted by a straight line, as for instance by the straight line $1'-3''$. To achieve this, it is sufficient to change in *Fig. 70b* the direction of voltage $-k_1V$ in comparison to voltage V_{C1} when V passes through zero, i. e. to change over the winding terminals connected to points a and b. Hereafter whilst the absolute value of V is growing, the voltage feeding the quadrature-axis winding will diminish according to the straight line $1'-3''$ (*Fig. 70c*).

From the foregoing it follows that the diagram of *Fig. 70b*, in which no auxiliary brushes are provided, can be used when no great accuracy in the automatic control is needed, especially in those cases, when the voltage has to be varied from a maximal value to zero. If technical conditions allow a commutation of the circuit carrying the exciting current I_e, this circuit diagram may be used also for autodynes, in which the voltage should be varied from a maximum positive value to a maximum negative value.

If the voltage of the autodyne is not required to vary until zero, the accuracy is enhanced by substituting a straight line for the corresponding circle section. Let us assume, for instance, an autodyne designed for charging storage batteries (*Fig. 18*). Should V vary in the proportion $1 : 0\cdot7$ (i. e. the proportion of abscissae of points 3 and 2 in *Fig. 70a)*, practically no error will arise by substituting the arc of the circle between points 2 and 3 by the straight line

$$V_{C2} - k_2 V$$

where

$$V_{C2} > V_{C1} \text{ and } k_2 > k_1$$

Hence, the circuit diagram in *Fig. 70b* can always be used, e. g., for charging batteries or supplying circuits with stabilized voltage, etc.*

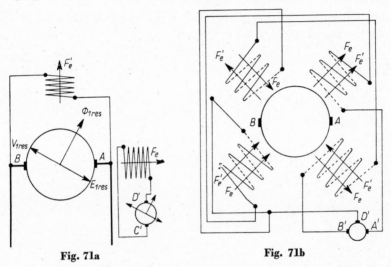

Fig. 71a   **Fig. 71b**

    The second expedient can be used in case of medium- and high-capacity autodynes, in whatever fields of use and under whatever technical conditions. It consists in taking the exciting current from a small auxiliary autodyne *(Fig. 71a)*, supplied from the same network as the main autodyne and arranged on a common axis. Thus synchronous operation can be ensured without the use of its own control windings.

    Since for the main and auxiliary autodynes the corresponding position of vectors $\overline{V}_{1res}$, $\overline{E}_{1res}$ and $\overline{\Phi}_{1res}$ have to coincide, the distribution of electrical potentials along the commutator circumference has to be equal in both machines. It follows that the brushes C' and D' of the auxiliary autodyne may be used instead of brushes C and D

---

    * *Chapter 17* contains diagrams of connections in which the scheme mentioned above does not affect accuracy.

(Fig. 71a). This figure shows the use of the auxiliary machine for feeding one of the two windings producing, as in *Fig. 65*, a direct-axis mmf F'_e and a quadrature-axis mmf F_e.

By using the magnet system according to *Fig. 58a*, the quadrature-axis windings may be arranged like the compensating windings of a d-c machine.

By using a magnet system as shown in *Fig. 59*, the exciting windings can be arranged as in *Fig. 68* with the difference that the winding terminals, connected in *Fig. 68* to brushes *A*, *B* and *D* of the autodyne, are connected now with the corresponding brushes *A'*, *B'* and *D'* of the auxiliary autodyne *(Fig. 71b)*.

ELIMINATION OF INTERNAL TORQUES
IN THE AUTODYNE

As stated above, the unevenness of the air gap in *Fig. 59*, the presence of magnetic saturation and, finally, the stator windings for slip excitation provoke practically no torque that could accelerate or decelerate the armature. There are, however, many other factors creating such torques, and therefore it is necessary to examine the possibilities of their elimination.

Such factors are, e. g., the bearing friction, the brush friction and the winding losses.

Since the speed of the auto-dyne is constant, the braking torque caused by friction may also be assumed practically constant. Therefore the elimination of the influence of friction upon the control properties of the autodyne requires a motor torque, which should be constant and independent of angle β.

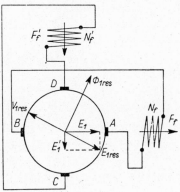

Fig. 72

Such a torque may be created, for instance, by windings N_f and N'_f shown in *Fig. 72*.

This system may be figured as being developed from the windings according to *Fig. 65*, if the terminals of the winding, acting along the direct axis, are changed over from brushes A and B to brushes C and D and the terminals of the winding, acting along the quadrature axis, from brushes C and D to brushes A and B. In this case this latter winding is supplied by voltage $E = c_1 E_1$ and, consequently, its mmf will be

$$F_f = c_7 E \tag{77}$$

directed to the right and provoking a compensating current $c_2 c_7 E =$

$= c_2 c_7 c_1 E_{1res} \cos \beta$ coinciding in direction with $- E_1$ and producing a motor power $3 c_2 c_7 c_1 E_{1res}^2 \cos^2 \beta$.

Analogously, the direct-axis winding, supplied now by E', producing the mmf

$$F_f' = c_7 E' \tag{78}$$

will build up the compensating current $c_2 c_7 E' = c_2 c_7 c_1 E_{1res} \sin \beta$, coinciding in direction with $-E_1'$ and creating a motor power $3 c_2 c_7 c_1 E_{1res}^2 \sin^2 \beta$. Considering that $E_{1res} \cong V_{1res}$, the total power produced by both windings is

$$3\, c_2 c_7 c_1 V_{1res}^2 (\sin^2 \beta + \cos^2 \beta) = \text{constant}$$

In this way the accelerating torque produced is constant and independent of β. Therefore, by the adequate choice of the constant c_7, i.e. of the number of turns and the cross section of windings, we obtain a torque equal in magnitude to the frictional torque (or even somewhat greater), apt to compensate the frictional torque. For this reason, this winding will be termed the friction-compensating winding.

Fig. 73 shows test results concerning the influence of the friction-compensating winding in the experimental machine of the MITE.

In order to investigate this problem, the machine was started asynchronously, and after attaining the normal slip, the system of friction-compensating winding was inserted.

By enlarging the maximum value of the current in these windings (i. e. by diminishing the resistances in their circuits), and by

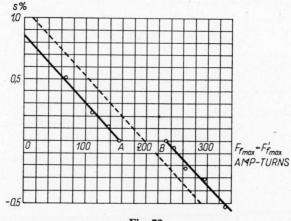

Fig. 73

measuring the value of slip by twice the number of oscillations of the pointer of a moving coil meter, connected to the d-c side of the machine, the dependence of the slip s (in per cent) is obtained in function of the maximum mmf $F_{f\max}$ of the friction-compensating winding.

The test result has showed that the slip varies proportionally to the variation of the friction-compensating mmf. At a definite value of this mmf (point A), the machine reaches synchronous speed ($s = 0$), i. e. the self-synchronizing of the autodyne is achieved.

Any further enlarging of the mmfs of windings N_f and N_f' causes an overcompensation of the frictional torque; consequently, the machine passes from synchronous run to an asyn-

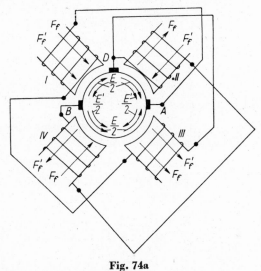

Fig. 74a

chronous one. The speed, however, will be higher than the synchronous one corresponding to network frequency, i. e. in our case at $f = 50$ cps, $n > 3000$ rpm and, consequently, a "negative slip" will arise.

The discontinuity of the mmf at $s = 0$ (section AB) is determined by the torque due to hysteresis, changing its direction with the changes in the sign of the slip ($n > n_s$).* The dotted straight line in *Fig. 73* would be obtained by neglecting the hysteresis.

By reversing the terminals of the friction-compensating windings, the slip of the machine increases, since the winding system produces a torque, not directed against the frictional torque but coinciding with it in direction.

Similarly to the replacement of the winding system of *Fig. 65* by that of *Fig. 68*, certain advantages might be achieved by replacing the winding system of *Fig. 72* by the system of *Fig. 74a*. The latter

---

* It may seem that eddy currents in the stator should cause a similar torque. It is, however, to be considered that this — unlike the form of the hysteresis loop practically independent of slip — will decrease proportionally to the slip and may therefore be practically neglected when close to synchronism.

can be conceived as obtained from the winding system of *Fig. 68,* by supplying the coils of half poles I and III not from brushes D and B, but from brushes D and A, and by feeding the coils of half poles II

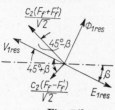

Fig. 74b

and III, not from brushes A and D but from brushes D and B. As shown by the arrows, the mmf of half poles I and III has now the value $F_f + F'_f$ equal to $c_7 (E + E')$. It sets up a compensating current

$$c_2 \frac{(F_f + F'_f)}{\sqrt 2}$$

which forms an angle $45° - \beta$ with voltage V_{1res} *(Fig. 74b).* Consequently, a motor power is created

$$\frac{3\,c_2 c_7 E_{1res}(E + E')}{\sqrt 2} \cos (45° - \beta) \simeq \frac{3 c_1 c_2 c_7 V^2_{1res}}{2} (\cos \beta + \sin \beta)^2$$

Similarly, the windings of half poles II and IV have the mmf $F_f + F'_f = c_7(E - E')$, which provokes a compensating current

$$\frac{c_2(F_f - F'_f)}{\sqrt 2}$$

including with vector $\overline{V_{1res}}$ an angle $45° + \beta$. Therefore a motor power

$$\frac{3 c_2 c_7 E_{1res}(E - E') \cos (45° + \beta)}{\sqrt 2} \simeq \frac{3 c_1 c_2 c_7 V^2_{1res}}{2} (\cos \beta - \sin \beta)^2$$

is created, whence the total motor power is

$$\frac{3 c_1 c_2 c_7 V^2_{1res}}{2} (2 \cos^2 \beta + 2 \sin^2 \beta) = 3 c_1 c_2 c_7 V^2_{1res} = \text{constant} \quad (79)$$

It might be seen that the corresponding torque is also constant and can therefore be used to compensate the frictional torque.

The effect dealt with may be achieved by the adequate choice of the quantities in an autodyne of any configuration.

If in any one autodyne the control or regulating windings are connected as shown in *Figs. 65, 68, 72* or *74,* the corresponding windings, having the same connections and acting along the same axis, can be united. This may be very economical if the mmf's of two windings are opposite to each other and can, therefore, be substituted by one winding, the mmf of which is equal to the difference of mmf's of the two windings. As an example, *Fig. 43* or *47* can be referred to, in which the control windings, arranged along the direct axis and supplied from brushes C and D, have a mmf opposite to the mmf F_f' according to *Fig. 72*.

If we have to do with a configuration according to *Fig. 58a*, where the use of auxiliary brushes C and D is not possible, it is best to start from what was said in connection with *Fig. 70b*. In this way the mmf F_f may be obtained by the aid of brushes A and B *(Fig. 72)*, while the mmf F_f' by connecting the direct-axis winding *(Fig. 75)* between voltage V_C and voltage k_1V, prevailing between points a and b of

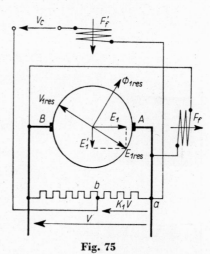

Fig. 75

the shunt resistance. *Figs. 76a* and *76b* are obtained by replacing the brushes of the autodyne by the brushes of the auxiliary autodyne mounted on the same shaft. *Fig. 76a* corresponds to the diagram, in which the brushes C and D of the main autodyne *(Fig. 72)* are re-

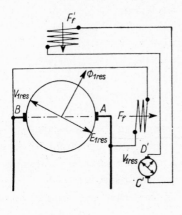

Fig. 76a

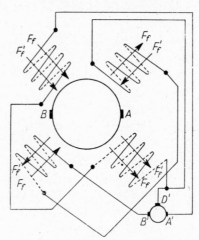

Fig. 76b

placed by brushes C' and D' of the auxiliary autodyne, while *Fig.* *76b* to the diagram where brushes A, B and D of the main autodyne *(Fig. 74a)* are replaced by the brushes A', B' and D' of the auxiliary autodyne.

While the auxiliary autodynes shown in *Figs. 71* and *76a*, *76b* are mounted on the shaft of the main autodyne, such diagrams also may be developed, in which the auxiliary autodyne is placed elsewhere and yields practically the same result. For this purpose the property of the autodyne, described in *Chapter 8* in connection with Eqs. (33) and (34), can be made use of.

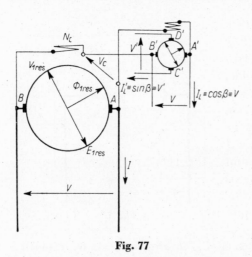

Fig. 77

This is exemplified in *Fig. 77*. Here the currents I_L and I'_L are produced by an auxiliary autodyne, controlled by the same voltage V_c as the main autodyne. Since angles β are thereby practically equal in both machines, currents I_L and I'_L can be made to feed the windings of the stator slip excitation and also to supply the friction-compensating winding in the main autodyne (in *Fig. 77* the latter is not shown). Thus the same result is achieved as in *Figs. 71a, 76a, 76b*, i. e. the main autodyne can be built without direct-axis brushes. Thus — as stated already — the auxiliary autodyne need not necessarily be arranged on the shaft of the main autodyne, but may be placed elsewhere. In *Fig. 77* the accuracy of control is somewhat smaller than in *Figs. 71a* and *76a, 76b*, in which the coincidence of angles β in both machines is secured by mechanical coupling.

Beside the internal torque created by friction, an internal electrodynamic torque is also provoked by higher harmonics when the autodyne is loaded. As is well-known, the mmf created by the direct current I *(Fig. 78a)*, is distributed along the armature circumference according to the triangle $1-2-3$ *(Fig. 78b)*, while the mmf of the compensating three-phase load current I_1 *(Fig. 78a)* is distributed according to a sine wave $1-4-3$. If the spatial fundamental wave

of the d-c mmf is supposed to equal the a-c mmf, the spatial
higher harmonics of the triangular mmf, as seen from *Fig. 78b*, remain
uncompensated. In addition, the magnetic flux Φ', owing to the special form of the magnet system, is distributed along the armature circumference, as shown in *Fig. 78c*, where the part of the flux passing
through half poles I and IV *(Fig. 68)* corresponds to the rectangle

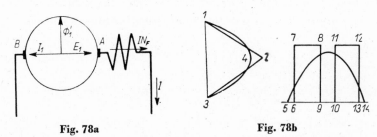

Fig. 78a   Fig. 78b

$6-7-8-9$, while the part of flux acting through half poles II and III
corresponds to the rectangle $10-11-12-13$. That is why it comprises,
besides the fundamental wave Φ'_1, higher harmonics also. The higher
harmonics of flux Φ' produce a supplementary torque with the corresponding higher harmonics of the mmf created by armature current
I. This torque is proportional to the product of current I and internal
voltage E_1, i. e. it is proportional to $IE_{1res} \cos \beta$.

This braking torque can be eliminated easily by a series coil
(Fig. 78a), by the so-called forcing winding with the number of
turns N_F and arranged along the quadrature-axis of the machine in
such a way that its mmf IN_F should be opposite to the mmf created
by the alternating current I_1. This coil will henceforth be referred to as
the quadrature-axis series coil or forcing winding.

In much the same way as was explained in connection with
mmf F_e *(Fig. 65a)* and mmf F_f *(Fig. 72)*, the mmf IN_F produces
a motor power and an accelerating torque, proportional to
$IN_F E_{1res} \cos \beta$. With this torque and by the adequate choice of
quantity N_F, the braking torque mentioned above can be compensated.

Because of the higher harmonics of the mmf produced by
the d-c current, one more electrodynamic torque arises. Suppose
that $\beta = 0$, i. e. $\Phi'_1 = \Phi'_{1max} = \Phi_{1res}$ *(Fig. 79a)*, that E_{1res} acts along
the quadrature axis and that the internal torques provoked by cur-
rents I and I_1 compensate each other. In this case — as seen from

Fig. 79a — the a-c mmf (sine wave 1, 4, 3) is equal to the fundamental wave of the d-c mmf (triangle 1, 2, 3).

Meanwhile the a-c mmf under the half poles I, II, III and
IV *(Fig. 68)* is greater than the d-c mmf *(Fig. 79b)*. This remaining
mmf (the area shaded in *Fig. 79b)* produces two branches of a quadrature-axis flux Φ_q *(Fig. 79a)*. The latter induces in the armature an
emf acting along the direct axis, which, in turn, provokes in
the three-phase armature winding, compensating currents I_{1C} oppo-

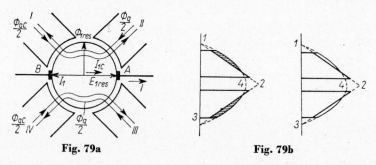

Fig. 79a   Fig. 79b

site in direction to flux Φ_q. Current I_{1C} produces a quadrature-axis
flux Φ_{qC} opposite to Φ_q, inducing a direct-axis emf of opposite
direction. Consequently, the algebraic sum of emfs induced in the
direct axis is zero. Thus the internal emf E_{1res} acts — as explained
above — only along the quadrature-axis.

In other words, the alternating current is equal in magnitude
to $I_1 - I_{1C}$, the a-c mmf (sine wave 1, 4', 3 in *Fig. 79c)* under
the half poles equals on an average the d-c mmf and therefore the
alternating current does not provoke any quadrature-axis flux.

Since, however, the a - c mmf created by $I_1 - I_{1C}$ is smaller
than the fundamental wave of the d-c mmf, the remaining mmf
provoked by current I_{1C} produces with flux $\Phi'_{1max} = \Phi_{1r\ s}$ a braking
torque also proportional to current I and to voltage E_{1res}.

Whenever the voltage acting along the quadrature axis is
not E_{1res} but only the component $E_{1res} \cos \beta$, and the direct-axis flux is
not Φ_{1res} but only $\Phi_{1res} \cos \beta$, the torque provoked will generally be
proportionate to $IE_{1res} \cos \beta$. Hence the torque produced by current
I_{1C} can be completely eliminated by adequately enlarging the number
of turns N_F calculated according to *Fig. 78*. This is supported also by
the results of tests carried out on the experimental machine of the
MITE.

For compensating this torque, the mmf of the friction-compensating quadrature-axis winding N_f was enlarged until the autodyne, in spite of this torque, was brought again to the state of $\beta = 0$.

The difference in the mmfs of winding N_f, required for compensating the internal torques at no load and full load, corresponds to the necessary mmf of the quadrature-axis series coil.

The dependence of the mmf of the quadrature-axis series coil on the load current, as obtained experimentally, is shown in *Fig. 80*.

The tangent of the slope of the straight line, substitutable for this curve, corresponds to the number of turns of the quadrature-axis series coil necessary to compensate the braking torque created by the two factors discussed above. At mains voltage $V_{1res} = 120$ V, the quadrature-axis series coil was found to require,

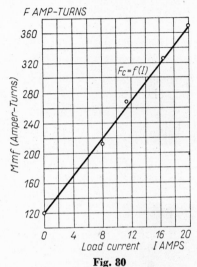

Fig. 80

on the basis of experiments .... 12·4 turns
by calculation .... 12 turns.

Thus the experiment proved the correctness of the basic equations deduced for designing the quadrature-axis series coil.

Having determined experimentally the number of turns required for this winding, the next step was to investigate its mode of operation. For this purpose the autodyne operating at $\beta = 45°$ with disconnected quadrature-axis series coil was loaded and the voltage between the direct-axis and quadrature-axis brushes, respectively, was measured. These voltages varied as follows:

between the quadrature-axis brushes at no-load ...... 143 V
,, the direct-axis ,, ,, ,, ... 138 V
,, the quadrature-axis ,, ,, 18·5 A load ...... 166 V
,, the direct-axis ,, ,, 18·5 A load ..... 30 V

The test results show an essential torque created for the reasons mentioned. This torque causes a deceleration of the autodyne armature, producing a voltage increase $\Delta V = 23$ V between the quadrature-axis brushes and a voltage decrease $-\Delta V' = 108$ V between the direct-axis brushes, i. e. a change of angle β by $34°$.

Later a similar experiment was carried out with an inserted quadrature-axis series coil of adequate number of turns. The voltage between the quadrature-axis brushes then remained unchanged.

This experiment shows that the braking torque due to the above-mentioned reasons was totally compensated by the quadrature-axis series coil.

When the number of turns of the quadrature-axis series coil was chosen greater than the one obtained by calculations (15 turns), the voltage between the quadrature-axis brushes decreased to 135 V, testifying to an overcompensation of the decelerating torque.

Thus the test results have given satisfactory proof of the possibility of compensating — by using the quadrature-axis series coil — the torque set up by the higher harmonics of d-c mmf in the armature.

CHAPTER 14

ACCURACY OF AUTOMATIC CONTROL
IN THE AUTODYNE

The foregoing chapters have been devoted to the investigation of ensuring a state of indifferent equilibrium of flux Φ_{1res} in the autodyne operating under steady-state conditions.

Nevertheless, even after the introduction of such measures, any change in the external conditions (such as the change in the supply voltage, variations of load, etc.) and the influence of hysteresis and saturation, may create small torques in the autodyne, causing certain deviations from the ideal law of control determined in the different connections.

In the derived equations above, characterizing the law of automatic control of the investigated autodyne, the value of voltage $V_{1r\ s}$ of the a-c mains is not included, meaning that it does not affect the law of control in principle. This may be explained by considering, for instance, that, while $V_{1r\ s}$ and E_{1res} increase, the impulse of the mmf $-\Delta F'$, due to changes in V in the control winding, sets up an accelerating torque causing $\overline{\Phi_{1r\ s}}$, $\overline{V_{1r\ s}}$ and $\overline{E_{1r\ s}}$ to rotate clockwise to a new position, in which the decrease of $\cos \beta$ compensates the influence of increasing $E_{1r\ s}$ upon $E = c_1 E_{1res} \cos \beta$.

There is, however, a condition creating a small torque at any variation of $V_{1r\ s}$. As was expounded in *Chapter 13*, the windings compensating the influence of frictional torque, produce a torque proportional to $V_{1r\ s}^2$.

Any change in V_{1res} alters the compensating torque, i. e. produces a braking or driving residual torque. It should be emphasized, however, that at voltage variations occurring in three-phase networks, in practice this residual torque has a relatively small value, because at variations of mains voltage within the range of $+5$ to -10 per cent, its value amounts to no more than to ±16 per cent of the frictional torque.

8*

Assume now that this torque accelerates the armature. In this case, V and I in the autodyne decrease (see *Fig. 16)*, until the residual mmf $i_c N_c' - IN'$ creates a generator power and a braking torque in compliance with it, compensating the residual torque mentioned above. Consequently, in steady-state condition, instead of Eq. (13), the following equation is valid:

$$(i_c N_c' - IN') \sin \beta = C_R \tag{80}$$

where C_R is a quantity proportional to the residual torque.

Now the mmf deviates from its ideal value by F_r causing a certain error. The value of this mmf is in the given case

$$F_r = \frac{C_R}{\sin \beta} \tag{81}$$

while the law of control is expressed by

$$I = \frac{i_c N_c'}{N'} - \frac{C_R}{N' \sin \beta} \tag{82}$$

As a consequence, we obtain the characteristic $I = f(V)$ *(Fig. 81)* instead of characteristics $1-2$ or $6-7$ *(Fig. 17)*. As can be seen, at quantities β being nearly zero, i. e. at quantities V being nearly equal to $V_{\max}$, the deviation from the ideal law of control $I = \text{const}$, increases rather quickly, while in the remaining range the

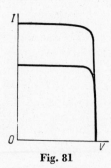

Fig. 81

deviation is, at an adequate choice of the quantities, comparatively small. It follows that, with autodynes described in *Chapter 8*, an automatic stabilization of the quantities is possible only up to a certain minimal value $\beta_{\min}$, which is generally about $20°$. This means a somewhat lower utilization of the machines in ratio $\cos 20° : \cos 0 = 0.94$, i. e. 94 per cent.

An adequately accurate control in the whole range $0° < \beta < 90°$ can be achieved by using the circuit diagram of *Fig. 53*, when $N_c/N_c' = N/N'$. In this case, by taking into consideration quantity C_R, we have, instead of Eq. (82), the following formula:

$$I = i_c \frac{N_c'}{N'} - \frac{C_R}{N \cos \beta + N' \sin \beta} = i_c \frac{N_c'}{N'} - \frac{C_R c_1 V_{1\text{res}}}{NV + N' \sqrt{V_{\max}^2 - U^2}} \tag{83}$$

Consequently, the deviation at $\beta = 0°$ is no longer infinite.

In the special case when $N = N'$ and $N_c = N'_c$, i. e. when using the diagram of connections in Fig. 54, Eq. (83) takes the following form:

$$I = i_c \frac{N'_c}{N'} - \frac{C_R}{N(\cos\beta + \sin\beta)} = i_c \frac{N'_c}{N'} - \frac{C_R c_1 V_{1\mathrm{res}}}{N(V + \sqrt{V^2_{\max} - V^2})} \qquad (84)$$

Since, in the range $0° < \beta < 90°$, the value of $\cos\beta + \sin\beta$ varies only within the limits 1 to and 1·41, the current I varies in this case only by

$$\pm \frac{0·205 \, C_R}{1·205 \, N}$$

i. e. it remains, with normal values of C_R, practically constant.

The relative error arising at the control of current I, i. e. the degree of inaccuracy is expressed in percentages

$$\frac{100 \, F_r}{i_{c\max} N'_c} = \frac{100 \, F_r}{F'_{c\max}} \qquad (85)$$

where $F'_{c\max}$ is the maximum value of mmf set up by the reference value. In the autodyne, e. g., in which $V = V_c$ is maintained as shown in *Fig. 23*, the quantity $F'_{c\max}$ will be:

$$F'_{c\max} = \frac{V_{c\max} N'_c}{r'_c} \qquad (86)$$

and the relative inaccuracy

$$\frac{100 \, F_r \, r'_c}{V_{c\max} N'_c} = \frac{100 \, (V_c - V)}{V_{c\max}} \qquad (87)$$

where r'_c is the resistance of the control winding. The same result might be obtained on the basis of the following considerations.

In order to achieve a mmf F_r in an autodyne with the law of control $V = V_c$, a current i_c should be created to pass through winding N'_c. At steady state in the autodyne and no internal torques, $i_c = 0$ because $V_c - V = 0$.

In the case investigated here, however, owing to the deviation between the voltages V_c and V, a current

$$i_c = \frac{V_c - V}{r'_c} \qquad (88)$$

arises. In this way we arrive at

$$i_c N'_c = F_r = \frac{(V_c - V) N'_c}{r'_c} \qquad (89)$$

It follows that the relative inaccuracy of control is in reality expressed by Eq. (87).

For investigating the deviation of the voltage of the autodyne from the reference value, the control characteristic of the auto-

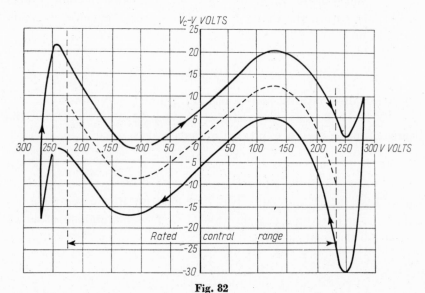

Fig. 82

dyne was examined by varying the control voltage from $+V_{max}$ to $-V_{max}$ and vice versa; i. e. the dependence $(V'_c - V) = f(V)$ was determined for mains voltage $V_{1res} = 220$ V.

Fig. 82 shows test results of the autodynes $A-2B$, $A-3B$ and $A-6B$. The curves $(V_c - V) = f(V)$ obtained in these tests have a character of a loop, which might be explained by hysteresis not eliminated during these experiments. By eliminating the hysteresis, we should arrive at the dotted curve *(Fig. 82)*. Its form is explained by the influence of non-compensated reluctance torque, arising because of the uneven permeance along the different axes of the machine. Its effect — as follows from theoretical considerations — appears especially at angles β, when the torque created by flux $\overline{\Phi_{1res}}$ and the mmf acting along the quadrature axis, conditioned by uneven permeance, is great. The dotted curve shows obviously the theoretical result, i. e. that the reluctance torque varies proportionally to $\sin 4\beta$ (see *Chapter 11*). If $V = 0$ (i. e. $\beta = \pi/2$) and $V = \pm\ 200$ V (i. e. $\beta \simeq \pi/4$), it is equal to zero; in the range of maximum voltages, in the neighbourhood of $\beta = 0$, it approaches again zero.

The influence of the changes in the mains voltage and the influence of the parameters of the control winding upon the

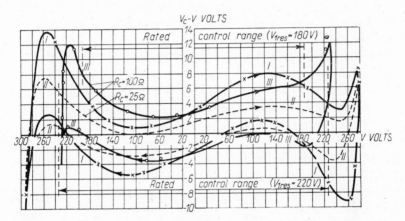

Fig. 83

magnitude of error in control were also investigated by the experiments.

For this purpose the control characteristics were tested for different mains voltages ($V_{1\mathrm{res}} = 220$ V and 180 V) and different resistances of the control winding ($r_c' = 100$ and 25 Ω).

Fig. 83 shows the results of these investigations the in form of curves $(V_c - V) = f(V)$. A decrease in the mains voltage caused a corresponding decrease in deviations due to reluctance torque. This is in compliance with theory, as by diminishing the voltage $\overline{V}_{1\mathrm{res}}$ the magnetic flux $\overline{\Phi}_{1\mathrm{r\ s}}$, as well as the reluctance torque varying proportionally to $\Phi_{1\mathrm{r\ s}}^2$, diminish.

The curves in *Fig. 83* also show that any reduction in the resistance of the control winding results in an adequate decrease of the voltage deviation $V_c - V$. This too is in complete conformity with theoretical considerations, the voltage deviation being

$$V_c - V = i_c\,r_c'$$

Since the current i_c is dependent upon the mmf F_r which is, in turn, determined by the inner inaccuracies of the machine in question, the current i_c will remain constant at the given inaccuracies and at the given voltage $V_{1r\,s}$, i. e. at the flux Φ_{1res}. Consequently, the value of voltage deviation $V_c - V$ will be proportional to the resistance.

In the machine A—3B at no-load, the maximum value of voltage deviation was found to vary

1. from $+12\cdot3$ V to $-6\cdot8$ V at voltage $V_{1res} = 220$ V and with series-connected control windings yielding $r_c' = 100\ \Omega$ (see curve I in *Fig. 83)*;

2. from $+8$ V to $-3\cdot5$ V at voltage $V_{1res} = 180$ V and with series-connected control windings (see curve III in *Fig. 83)*;

3. from $+5\cdot75$ V to -3 V at voltage $V_{1res} = 220$ V and with control windings connected parallel in series yielding $r_c' = 25\ \Omega$ (see curve II in *Fig. 83)*. It follows that in this case the autodyne ensures the accuracy of coincidence of the voltage V, to be controlled with the reference value V_c within the limits $+2\cdot5$ to $-1\cdot3$ per cent of rated d-c voltage 230 V.

The value of mmf F_r, due to the variation of the mains voltage, can be lowered in many fields of application by a number of measures. Thus, for instance, in *Chapter 6* the value i_c in the connections of *Figs. 16* and *18* was assumed to represent a constant quantity, not depending on the parameters of the autodyne and therefore also independent of the mains voltage.

If, however, current i_c is produced by a voltage V_c varying with the value V_{1res} according to the law

$$V_c = c_8 V_{1res} \pm c_8' \tag{90}$$

(where c_8 and c_8' are constants), then i_c also decreases with decreasing voltage $V_{1r\,s}$. Consequently, the deviation from value I and the quantity F_r may be essentially diminished and, under certain conditions, even totally eliminated.

In the AZ type autodynes whose technical specifications do not require a high degree of accuracy, the voltage V_c is taken from the a-c mains through a rectifier, i. e. c_8' is chosen practically zero.

Thus the voltage V is, in reality, not maintained constant in the machine of the *AZ* type but proportional to V_{1res}. The residual torque, mentioned above however, acts in the opposite sense when affected by changes in V_{1res}. This results in voltage V varying but little with varying V_{1res}.

The influence of mains voltage variation upon the accuracy of control in the autodyne was investigated on the basis of *Fig. 23* at no load and under load.

The tests were carried out for different control voltages and different mains voltages.

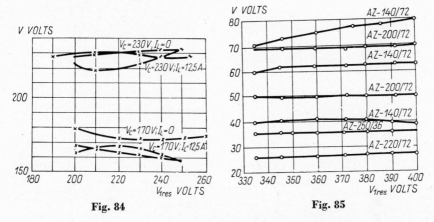

Fig. 84   Fig. 85

The test results concerning the autodyne A—3B are shown in *Fig. 84*. The deviations of curves $V = f(V_{1res})$ from the constant values are explained exactly by the change in accuracy, by which the frictional torque is compensated. Those changes were observed as long as the torque created by the friction-compensating coil depended on the value E_{1res}^2, i. e. on the square of the mains voltage. The fact that the curves $V = f(V_{1res})$ do not coincide when increasing or decreasing the voltage V_{1res}, is due to hysteresis in the stator yoke.

The maximum voltage variation of the autodyne was $\pm 7 \cdot 5$ V, i. e. $\pm 3 \cdot 25$ per cent, when the mains voltage varied 22 per cent.

Fig. 85 shows the dependence $V = f(V_{1res})$ for three AZ type autodynes of the experimental series, two of which were tested with three different values of V. These curves show that a variation of mains voltage within the range from $+5$ per cent to -10 per cent has but very little effect on the output voltage of the autodyne.

In addition to these tests, the influence of mains voltage variations upon the accuracy of control was investigated experimentally in an autodyne stabilizing the load current I.

Fig. 86 shows the dependence of load current on the mains voltage at different control currents in the AZ—140/72 type autodyne connected to a constant voltage source (to a d-c generator).

As shown by these curves, an increase in the mains voltage provokes — as follows from the theory of the autodyne — an adequate decrease of the load current. With load current $I = 135$ A, a mains

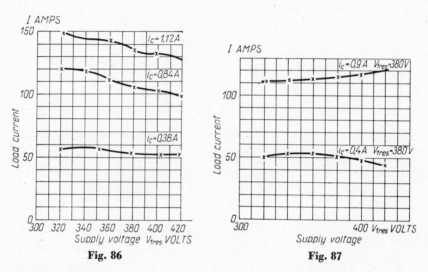

Fig. 86   **Fig. 87**

voltage variation of $+10$ to -15 per cent of the rated value, causes a variation of current from -6 A to $+15$ A, i. e. from $+4\cdot3$ to $-10\cdot7$ per cent of the rated current 140 A. With current $I = 53$ A a mains voltage variation within the same range causes a variation of current from $-0\cdot5$ A to $+4$ A, i. e. from $-0\cdot36$ to $+2\cdot9$ per cent.

In order to examine the possibility of compensating the load current variations occurring at mains voltage variation, the control winding of the autodyne was connected to a selenium rectifier, supplied by the same a-c mains as the slip rings of the autodyne. In this case the control current varies proportionally to the mains voltage.

Fig. 87 shows the dependence of load current I on the mains voltage in the AZ—140/72 type autodyne with the above-mentioned control-winding supply at a constant load voltage $V_L = 60$ V (voltage of a d-c generator) and with different values of control current. The curves obtained support the theoretical conclusions as to the possibility of compensating the load current variations due to the variation of mains voltage V_{1res}, by supplying the control winding from the mains voltage V_{1res}.

In the case here discussed, the said current variations at greater currents I were even overcompensated; consequently, with enlarged voltage V_{1res}, the current did not decrease but, on the contrary, increase. When the mains voltage was varied by $+10$ and -15 per cent of the rated value, changes by $+4\cdot7$ and $-3\cdot2$ per cent of the rated current 140 A occurred, respectively. At small currents the maximum variation did not exceed the limits ±4 A, i.e. amounted to $\pm7\cdot5$ per cent.

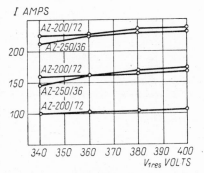

Fig.88 shows the characteristics $I = f(V_{1res})$ for types AZ—200/72 and AZ—250/36. The curves

Fig. 88

of type AZ—200/72 are conspicuous for the high degree of accuracy. With mains voltage variations by $+5$ and -10 per cent of the rated value, the load current varies, for instance, by 1 and $-2\cdot5$ per cent of the rated value. The curves $I = f(V_{1res})$ for the type AZ—250/36 have a somewhat greater slope.

It should be mentioned that in autodynes wich the task of setting up a voltage with only one definite unvariable reference value,

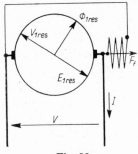

Fig. 89

the occurrence of a residual torque produced by the changes in voltage V_{1res} may practically be prevented on the basis of the following considerations.

The torque produced by the quadrature-axis winding, supplied from brushes A and B (*Fig. 72*), is proportional to $V_{1res}^2 \cos^2\beta$. Since $V \cong c_1 V_{1res} \cos\beta$ when maintaining $V = \text{constant}$, the quantity $V_{1res}^2 \cos^2\beta$ will also be constant. It follows that in the case mentioned, for compensating the frictional torque, it will be enough to use the winding shown in *Fig. 89*. In this case the variation of V_{1res} will produce no residual torques, because the influence of the variation of voltage V_{1res} upon the value of the friction-compensating torque, proportional to V_{1res}^2, is completely eliminated automatically by the opposite variation of $\cos^2 \beta$.

Fig. 90 shows the characteristics $V = f(V_{1res})$, at no load and under load, of the experimental machine of the MITE when a single quadrature-axis winding is inserted for compensating the frictional torque, in case the hysteresis is eliminated and the reluctance

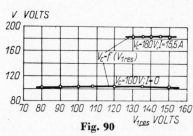

Fig. 90

torque is balanced by a torque, produced by supplying the direct-axis winding N_f' from an independent source. These characteristics show that, if the internal torques are adequately compensated, the voltage of the autodyne remains practically unchanged at varying mains voltage.

Thus, in the autodyne operating as a source of constant stabilized voltage, a very great accuracy of control can be obtained by the adequate choice of the connections of the stator windings.

The voltage drop in the armature winding caused by the load current affects the control law in the same way as the variation of V_{1res}.

Should the autodyne have no internal torques at all, the transition from no load to full load could have no influence on the control law, because neither the voltage drop nor the supply voltage V_{1res} are included in the equation expressing the control law of the idealized autodyne. If, e. g., in the autodyne *(Fig. 23)* ensuring $V = V_c$, the voltage V diminished owing to load in comparison to voltage V_{1res}, the current i_c arising hereby would produce a torque decelerating the armature, so that $\overline{\Phi_{1res}}$ and $\overline{V_{1res}}$ would rotate anti-clockwise, until a position in which the diminution of V caused by the voltage drop would be compensated by the increment of $\cos \beta$.

In reality, however, the voltage drop only slightly changes the electrodynamic torque necessary to compensate the frictional torque.

In the armature, along the direct axis, only very small currents flow through brush D; consequently their voltage drop can be completely neglected.

A voltage drop on the armature resistance will be produced only by the d-c current I and by the a-c current I_1 compensating the former and being practically proportional to it (if it is assumed that the winding of stator slip excitation eliminates the current I_{mres} and that the active component of the no-load current can be neglected in this case).

The inductive (or reactance) voltage drop in the direct axis of the armature, produced by current I_1, may practically be eliminated by the opposite voltage drop, produced in the phase winding by current I^*. Hence, if the direct-axis component of voltage V_{1res}, is denoted by V_1', then

$$E' = c_1 E_{1res} \sin \beta \cong c_1 V_1' = V' \tag{91}$$

If the specifications of an autodyne require the separation of d-c and a-c circuits in the armature, as, e. g., in the AZ type, the voltage drop arising in the a-c winding diminishes the vector $\overline{E_{1res} \cos \beta}$ in comparison to the component $\overline{V_{1res} \cos \beta}$ of voltage $\overline{V_{1res}}$, which will be denoted in the following by

$$V_1 = V_{1res} \cos \beta \tag{92}$$

In this way, according to Eq. (3), E also diminishes. Furthermore, in the d-c circuit the voltage V also diminishes as compared to E, i.e. to $c_1 E_{1res} \cos \beta$.

In most autodynes the a-c and d-c armature windings are partly or completely united. In this case the resistance voltage drops, caused by the direct current, and the alternating current counteract each other, therefore the decrease of quantities $E_{1res} \cos \beta$ and V will be much less.

By considering that voltage drops, caused by current I_1, are proportional also to I, the following equation is valid under load

$$\begin{aligned} V = E - aI &= c_1 E_{1res} \cos \beta - aI = \\ &= c_1(V_1 - bI) - aI = c_1 V_1 - (c_1 b + a) I \end{aligned} \tag{93}$$

where aI and bI are small voltage drops proportional to current I.

It follows that if the torque set up by the mmf F_f equals at no load

$$c_9 E E_{1res} \cos \beta = c_9 c_1 V_1^2$$

---

* Note: A detailed investigation of this rather complicated problem would exceed the limits of this book.

where c_9 is a constant, the torque under load will be

$$c_9 V E_{1res} \cos \beta = c_9 [c_1 (V_1 - bI) - aI] (V_1 - bI) =$$
$$= c_9 c_1 V_1^2 - 2 c_9 c_1 V_1 bI + c_9 c_1 b^2 I^2 - c_9 aI V_1 + c_9 ab I^2 \cong \qquad (94)$$
$$\cong c_9 c_1 V_1^2 - c_9 V_1 I (2 c_1 b + a)$$

if the very small quantities $c_9 c_1 b^2 I^2$ and $c_9 ab I^2$ are neglected.

The torque set up by the mmf E_f' is

$$c_9 E' E_{1res} \sin \beta = c_9 c_1 V_1'^2 \qquad (95)$$

both at no load and under load.

Hence the total torque at no load is

$$c_9 c_1 (V_1^2 + V_1'^2) = c_9 c_1 V_{1res}^2$$

and under load

$$c_9 c_1 V_1^2 + c_9 c_1 V_1'^2 - c_9 V_1 I (2 c_1 b + a)$$

i.e. it is diminished by

$$c_9 (2 c_1 b + a) I V_1 = (E_{1res} \cos \beta + bI) c_9 (2 c_1 b + a) I$$

By neglecting again the quantities $2 c_9 c_1 b^2 I^2$ and $c_9 ab I^2$, the voltage drop influencing the mmf F_f, will cause a residual braking torque in the armature

$$c_9 (2 c_1 b + a) I E_{1res} \cos \beta$$

This torque might be compensated by a certain increase of the number of turns on the series quadrature-axis coil (*Fig. 78a*), which produces — as stated above — an accelerating torque proportional to $I E_{1res} \cos \beta$.

Let us now investigate the effect of the change in V_{1res} on the torques, created by the mmfs F_e and F_e' in the winding system of stator slip excitation.

If $V_{1r\ s}$ is diminished, V_1 can generally be expected to decrease to $V_1 - \Delta V_1$ and V_1' to $V_1' - \Delta V_1'$. It follows that by neglecting, for the time being, the influence of voltage drops, the following equations are obtained:

$$V' = E' = c_1 E_{1res} \sin \beta = c_1 (V_1' - \Delta V_1) \qquad (96)$$

and

$$V = E = c_1 E_{1res} \cos \beta = c_1 (V_1 - \Delta V_1) \qquad (97)$$

Before the change in voltage $V_{1\mathrm{res}}$, the mmf F_e has created the driving torque

$$c_9' E' E_{1\mathrm{res}} \cos \beta = c_9' c_1 V_1' V_1$$

(where c_9' is a constant), and the mmf F_e' has created the braking torque

$$-c_9 E\, E_{1\mathrm{res}} \sin \beta = -\, c_9' c_1 V_1 V_1'$$

resulting in the sum of torques being zero. At a decrease of $V_{1\mathrm{res}}$ the driving torque will be

$$c_9' c_1 (V_1' - \varDelta V_1')\,(V_1 - \varDelta V_1)$$

and the braking torque

$$-c_9' c_1 (V_1 - \varDelta V_1)\,(V_1' - \varDelta V_1')$$

Consequently, no torque is produced by the winding system of slip excitation in spite of the changes in voltage $V_{1\mathrm{res}}$.

Let us investigate now the influence of voltage drop on the mode of operation of this system.

After the appearance of current I, the driving torque created by mmf F_e will be

$$c_9' c_1 V_1' (V_1 - bI)$$

and the braking torque produced by mmf F_e'

$$-c_9' V E_{1\mathrm{res}} \sin \beta = -\, c_9' [c_1 (V_1 - bI) - aI]\, V_1'$$

By summing up these torques, a residual driving torque

$$c_9' a I V_1' = c_9' a I E_{1\mathrm{res}} \sin \beta$$

is obtained.

This torque, owing to the influence of voltage drop on the performance of the system of exciting windings, can be eliminated completely by the aid of a mmf, acting along the direct axis, proportional to I and — as stated above — producing a torque proportional to $I E_{1\mathrm{res}} \sin \beta$. For this purpose it will be sufficient, for instance, to reduce adequately the resistance r_1 in the autodyne of *Fig. 34.* In the autodynes according to *Figs. 16* and *18*, considering that $I \equiv i_c$, i_c can be reduced accordingly, etc.

Consequently, the winding system of friction compensation causes, at any change of voltage $V_{1\mathrm{res}}$, the quantity to be controlled to deviate by a small amount from the law of control, but this deviation can be eliminated completely in certain cases and partly in others.

The system of slip excitation does not produce any deviation at the variation of voltage V_{1res}.

The operation of both systems is slightly altered by load producing small resultant torques. These, however, are opposed to each other and, in addition, can easily be compensated by creating adequate mmf's.

Let us briefly investigate the effect of hysteresis. This also produces internal torques in the machine, influencing thereby the law of control. Suppose, for instance, that the magnetic flux $\overline{\Phi_{1res}}$ in the autodyne *(Fig. 16)* rotates anticlockwise owing to the increase of R_L and V. The armature — as explained in *Chapter 6* — operates, for a short time, with a positive slip like an induction motor. Yet it is known that an accelerating torque is produced by hysteresis in the asynchronous machines. When the slip becomes negative, this torque too, changes its sign and the driving torque turns into a braking one. Analogously, at anticlockwise rotation of flux $\overline{\Phi_{1res}}$ in the autodyne, the hysteresis must create an accelerating torque and at clockwise rotation (in the case in question at a reduction of R_L and V) a braking torque. Since the steady-state condition (i.e. the synchronous one) can only be maintained in the autodyne if the algebraic sum of all torques acting on the shaft equals zero, the autodyne will control, on account of hysteresis, according to the law

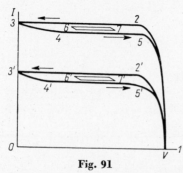

Fig. 91

$$(i_c N_c' - IN') \sin \beta = \pm C_H \quad (98)$$

where C_H is a quantity depending upon the action of hysteresis. The sign " $+$ " will be valid at positive slips and the sign " $-$ " at negative slips. In this way the current I at an increase of V will be somewhat smaller than $i_c N_c'/N'$ and at a decrease of V, somewhat greater.

Accordingly, in place of the curves of *Fig. 81*, we get, owing to hysteresis, the characteristics shown in *Fig. 91*. If, for instance, the machine is adjusted to control the current, when V reduces from V_{max} to zero, according to characteristic 1—2—3, i. e. to maintain it practically constant in the range 2—3, then, while V increases, the current will be regulated according to characteristic 3—4—5—1, i. e. again held practically constant in the range 4—5, though at a somewhat lower value. By diminishing the current i_c, the loop is lowered and we obtain, accordingly, the characteristic 1—2′—3′—4′—5′—1.

Fig. 92 shows load characteristics of the experimental autodyne of the MITE with stator excitation *(Fig. 54)*. Here curve B refers

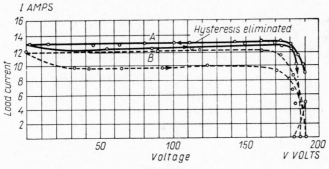

Fig. 92

to the experiment in which the hysteresis has a normal value. The comparatively great width of loop B may be explained by the low number of turns on winding N' carrying current I. However, it should be remembered that in Eq. (98) the deviation of I from the reference value, determined by i_c, is

$$\pm \frac{C_H}{N' \sin \beta}$$

i. e. inversely proportional to N'.

The deviation, obviously, does not depend upon the value of current I, as may be seen also in *Fig. 91*. This is corroborated also by the test results obtained with the experimental autodyne of the MITE shown in *Fig. 93*.

If the voltage varies (and $\overline{\Phi_{1res}}$ displaces) within narrow limits, as is the case when charging or discharging batteries, then the width of the loop decreases nearly proportionally to its length, and with a certain value of current i_c we, get the loop 6—7 and with another value, the loop 6′—7′ *(Fig. 91)*.

In many uses of the autodyne (as in charging batteries, when V varies in one direction only) the influence of hysteresis has practically no significance. Should it assume a significant value, it may be essentially diminished by adequately treating the iron, or by demagnetizing it with alternating current. Curve A in *Fig. 92* represents test results, showing that, by the aid of the latter, the width of the loop can be essentially lowered.

Internal torques may also arise in consequence of the saturation of the magnetic circuit, when the permeance of the machine at

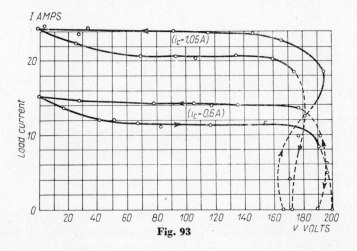

Fig. 93

$\beta = 45°$ differs from that at $\beta = 0°$ and $\beta = 90°$. In *Chapter 11* a method for computing units has been described, enabling us to reduce considerably the internal torques and the mmf F_r created by it.

Smaller torques may arise owing to inaccuracies in technology, e. g., to different thicknesses of the air gap along the armature circumference, etc.

The algebraic sum of all arising residual torques, due to quite different factors and acting partly opposite to each other, creates — as shown above — a corresponding mmf F_r, determining ultimately the deviation from the ideal law of control.

As Eq. (85) shows, beside the reduction of mmf F_r to the lowest possible value, there is another way of enhancing the accuracy of control of the autodynes. This consists in enlarging F'_{cmax} to a possible maximum value, e. g., in case of an autodyne holding I constant by increasing quantities N'_c and $i_c N'_c$; or in case of an autodyne maintaining $V = V_c$ by enlarging the cross section of the conductors, proportional to N'_c/r'_c.

CHAPTER 15

OTHER AUTODYNES WITH CONTROL WINDINGS ALONG TWO AXES

Further possibilities for changing the characteristics of the machines are obtained by adding different control windings, acting along the direct axis or along both axes of the machine, and supplied by

$$E \simeq V, \; E' \simeq V', \frac{E + E'}{2} \simeq \frac{V + V'}{2} \; \text{ or } \; \frac{E - E'}{2} \simeq \frac{V - V'}{2}$$

i. e. by all possible voltages prevailing between the different brushes on the commutator. Besides, the desired mmf's proportional to the enumerated voltages may also be obtained without adding any supplementary windings.

This may be explained by the fact that in the autodyne — as expounded in detail in *Chapters 12* and *13* — mmf's are set up by the mentioned voltages, are proportional to them and create the system of stator slip excitation, as well as the system of friction compensation.

It follows that by increasing or decreasing the mmf's of the above-mentioned system along certain axes or by changing their directions, the same result is achieved as if supplementary control windings, varying according to the same law, were added to the two existing winding systems. It should, however, be emphasized that the mmf of the winding in Fig. 43, supplied from the brushes C and D, is created in a similar way.

Here are some examples of realizing this method:

1. Let us choose $N' = 0$, $N_c = 0$ and $N_c' = 0$, i. e. out of the four windings of *Fig. 53* only the series winding remains, which is arranged along the quadrature axis. This creates a motor power $3E_{1\text{res}} \cos \beta \, c_2 I N$. Let us change now either the mmf's F_f and F_f' compensating the influence of friction, or possibly even their direction. *(Fig. 94a).* This is equivalent to the addition of a winding system-

creating a constant generator power of some c_{10} value. Thus by considering that $V \cong E = c_1 E_{1res} \cos \beta$, we obtain the equation

$$V I = \frac{c_{10} c_1}{3 c_2 N} = \text{constant} \tag{99}$$

i. e. the autodyne automatically maintains the power constant. By supplying a separately excited motor from such an autodyne, hyper-

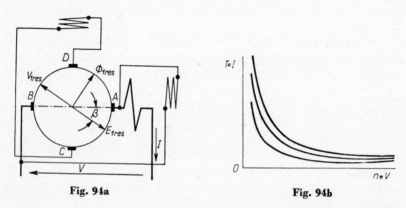

Fig. 94a   Fig. 94b

bolic mechanical characteristics are obtained, and, by varying the quantity c_{10}, a set of such curves may be obtained *(Fig. 94b)*.

2. When in an autodyne built according to *Fig. 54*, comprising in addition a friction-compensating winding according to *Fig. 72*, the mmf F_f is enlarged, the following equation is obtained

$$I = i_c \frac{N_c}{N} - c_{11} \frac{\cos^2 \beta}{N(\cos \beta + \sin \beta)} =$$

$$= i_c \frac{N_c}{N} - c_{11} \frac{V^2}{N(\sqrt{V_{max}^2 - V^2} + V)} \tag{100}$$

Some of these characteristics, whose shape can be altered by the variation of constant c_{11}, are shown in *Fig. 95*.

3. If in the autodyne of *Fig. 54* the mmf F_f of the quadrature-axis winding *(Fig. 72)* is enlarged and the mmf F_e of the quadrature-axis winding *(Fig. 65)* is also increased by the same amount, we get the following equation

$$I = i_c \frac{N_c}{N} - c_{12} \frac{\sin \beta \cos \beta + \cos^2 \beta}{N(\sin \beta + \cos \beta)} =$$

$$= \frac{i_c N_c}{N} - \frac{c_{12} \cos \beta}{N} = \frac{i_c N_c}{N} - \frac{c_{12}}{N \cdot c_1} \frac{V}{V_{1res}} \tag{101}$$

As characteristics of such a machine, a set of straight lines is obtained *(Fig. 96)*, the slope of which can be controlled by varying the quantity c_{12}.

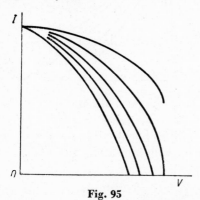

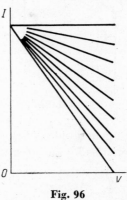

Fig. 95   Fig. 96

4. For an autodyne built according to *Fig. 97a*, in which F_f and F_f' are reduced and even their direction changed, the following equation is obtained:

$$I = \frac{c_{13}(\cos^2 \beta + \sin^2 \beta) - c_{14} \cos \beta}{N(\sin \beta + \cos \beta)} = \frac{c_{13} V_{max} - c_{14} V}{N(\sqrt{V_{max}^2 - V^2} + V)} \tag{102}$$

The form of characteristics obtained in this case is shown in *Fig. 97b* for a given quantity c_{13} and different values of c_{14}.

5. If the quantity c_{14} in *Fig. 97a* is chosen zero, i. e. if the quadrature-axis winding is eliminated and, in addition, the mmf F_e' *(Fig. 65)* is enlarged, the following equation is obtained:

$$I = \frac{c_{13}(\cos^2 \beta + \sin^2 \beta) + c_{15} \sin \beta \cos \beta}{N(\sin \beta + \cos \beta)} \tag{103}$$

By choosing $c_{15} = 0.82 \, c_{13}$, we obtain: $I \simeq$ const. In this case, it is possible to omit a control current i_c, that would be supplied from an external source, if the mains voltage can be regarded as constant.

These few examples, referring only to a single type of autodyne, namely to that which controls the load current automatically,

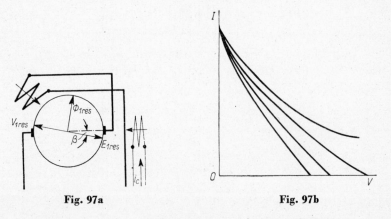

Fig. 97a   Fig. 97b

give a general idea of the vast possibilities for obtaining different characteristics by autodynes with control windings along two axes.

CHAPTER 16

POSSIBILITIES OF ESTABLISHING AND CONTROLLING REFERENCE VALUES

The reference values of autodynes (e. g. the voltage V_c in *Fig. 23* or the current i_c in *Figs. 16* and *18)* might be established and controlled in different well-known ways.

Such values may also be obtained by rectifying the mains voltage. In this case the voltage V_c or the current i_c will vary proportionally to the mains voltage and will change accordingly the quantities to be controlled (V or I). By taking into account the effect of the friction-compensating torque at any change in V_{1res}, as investigated in *Chapter 14*, we find that the influence of V_{1res} upon this torque diminishes the influence of V_{1rcs} upon V_c. This method of establishing a reference value is used in the AZ type machines.

If a more stable reference value is required, the rectifier can be supplied by a saturated transformer, or any other well-known method can be applied for stabilization.

Beyond certain rated powers, the autodyne may be equipped with auxiliary devices or machines for establishing a reference value, yielding characteristics of different shapes and simultaneously allowing the simplification of the general scheme. If, for instance, the autodyne is meant to stabilize V at an invariable reference voltage V_c, this can be achieved by a small generator with permanent magnetic field, mounted on the shaft of the autodyne.

Since the frequency of the network supplying the autodyne is generally stable and therefore the speed of the autodyne is practically constant, the voltage of the said generator will also be constant.

Instead of permanent magnets, the generator may have field coils supplied by an exciting current stabilized at a definite level. The poles may also be provided with other windings, e.g., such as carry the load current or are connected to voltages V_c, V_{1res} or to any arbitrary quantity.

This method of establishing a desired reference value is preferable, when it becomes necessary to switch over an autodyne operating according to a definite law of control, to another connection yielding another law of control. In such cases, the switching over of the load current may create inconveniences in operation. Therefore it may be of practical interest that the same effect of changing the form of the characteristic can be achieved by switching over the load circuit of a small auxiliary generator.

As an example, we mention a diagram of connections proposed by the author for autodynes, feeding d-c motors driving excavators or similar machines.

The electrical drive of such mechanisms often requires the speed of the motor to diminish until zero, when a certain limit value of external torque is reached, and to grow up to the rated one, when this torque decreases (excavator characteristic). Often the motor is required to keep a definite speed automatically constant, independent from load (e.g. the drive of the platform), even if the speed is very low. Finally, an automatic stabilization of torque, i. e. of motor current, according to a definite reference value, is sometimes required.

Obviously, such performance might be ensured by supplying a separately excited d-c motor from an autodyne. Here constant speed could be ensured by using the diagram of *Fig. 23*, whereas for a constant current and a constant torque, *Fig. 16* might be used. Here a switch-over from one diagram to another would involve the breaking of the load circuit.

This disadvantage can be eliminated by using an auxiliary autodyne.

Let us assume that *Figs. 23* and *16* are united as in *Fig. 98*. Here we have a winding N' carrying current I and a winding N'_c fulfilling at the same time the function of winding N'_c in *Fig. 23* (because it is connected to the difference of voltages V and V_c) and the function of winding N'_c in *Fig. 16* (because in steady state it carries current i_c). The voltage V_c is produced by an amplidyne *Amp* having a compensating winding K, eliminating totally the demagnetizing effect of the armature reaction in the direct axis. The amplidyne has, in addition, four coils, of which no. 1 is supplied by voltage V_c; no. 2 carries the direct current i for reference; no. 3 is fed by voltage V, when the switch S_1 is in position a; and winding no. 4 carries a current proportional to current I, when the switch S_2 is in position b, thereby connect, ing winding no. 3, parallel to the resistance of the primary coil of transformer T_2. Thus the mmf's of coils nos. 2, 3 and 4 are in opposition to the mmf of coil no. 1.

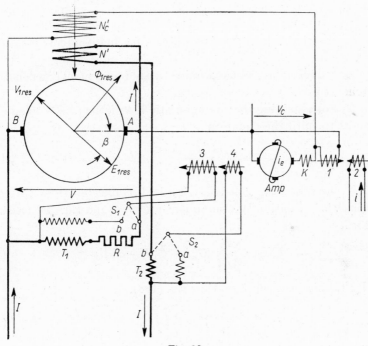

Fig. 98

By neglecting, for the first approximation, the direct-axis mmf building up the exciting current i_e in the quadrature axis of the amplidyne, we get the following equation:

$$C_1' V_c = C_2' i + C_3' V + C_4' I \tag{104}$$

where C_1', C_2', C_3' and C_4' are constants.

In addition, the following equations are valid (as for *Figs. 23* and *16*):

$$i_c = \frac{V_c - V}{r_c'} \tag{105}$$

and

$$IN' = i_c N_c' \tag{106}$$

By substituting the value of V_c from Eq. (104) into Eq. (105) and the value of i_c from Eq. (105) into Eq. (106), we have

$$IN' = \frac{N'_c}{r'_c C'_1}(C'_2 i + C'_3 V + C'_4 I - C'_1 V) \tag{107}$$

Thus, by the adequate choice of the constants, a set of load characteristics $V = f(I)$ is obtained, having completely different forms.

Furthermore, let us examine two borders, namely when $V \equiv i$ and when $I \equiv i$.

For obtaining the characteristic $V \equiv i$, the constants are chosen so as to fulfil the equation

$$\frac{C'_4}{C'_1} = \frac{N' r'_c}{N'_c} \tag{108}$$

Suppose now that coil no. 3 is disconnected from voltage V (switch S_1 is in position b). Consequently, $C'_3 = 0$ and Eq. (107) assumes the form

$$IN' = \frac{N'_c}{r'_c C'_1}(C'_2 i + C'_4 I - C'_1 V) \tag{109}$$

i. e. by taking into consideration Eq. (108),

$$V = \frac{C'_2}{C'_1} i \tag{110}$$

In other words: if coil no. 3 is disconnected, the autodyne has the same characteristic as if it were connected according to *Fig. 23*.

The result obtained can be physically explained on the basis of the simplified diagram of *Fig. 99*.

After disconnecting coil no. 3, Eq. (104) becomes

$$V_c = \frac{C'_2 i}{C'_1} + \frac{C'_4 I}{C'_1}$$

i. e. voltage V_c consists of two parts

$$\frac{C'_2 i}{C'_1}$$

and

$$\frac{C'_4 I}{C'_1}$$

corresponding to the mmf's $C_2'i$ and $C_4'I$ balancing the mmf $C_1'V_c$ in the amplidyne.

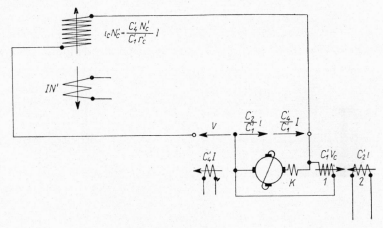

Fig. 99

On the other hand, according to the theory of the autodyne, $i_c N_c' = IN'$ or by considering Eq. (108)

$$i_c\, N_c' = I \frac{C_4'\, N_c'}{C_1'\, r_c'}$$

This mmf is obviously built up by the component $C_4'I/C_1'$ of the voltage V_c. Hence the algebraic sum of the other voltage components affecting i_c, i. e.

$$\frac{C_2'\, i}{C_1'} - V$$

should be equal to zero. In other words, the autodyne controls its voltage according to

$$V = \frac{C_2'\, i}{C_1'}$$

Should V vary by $+\varDelta V$, synchronizing mmf's

$$\pm \frac{\varDelta V}{r_c'}\, N_c'$$

would arise creating torques acting against the changes in V.

In order to obtain the characteristics $I \equiv i$, let us assume that the constants are chosen to fulfil

$$C_3' = C_1' \tag{111}$$

Let us assume furthermore that coil no. 3 is connected to voltage V (switch S_1 in *Fig. 98* is in position a), while coil no. 4 is

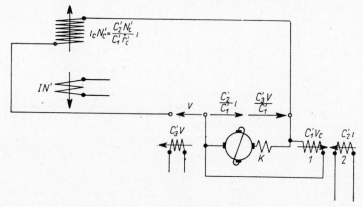

Fig. 100

disconnected from the circuit of current I (switch S_2 is in position a). Thus $C_4' = 0$ and Eq. (107) becomes

$$IN' = \frac{N_c'}{r_c' C_1'} (C_2' i + C_3' V - C_1' V) \tag{112}$$

i. e. by taking into consideration Eq. (111) we get

$$I = \frac{N_c' C_2'}{N' r_c' C_1} i \tag{113}$$

In other words the autodyne has now the characteristics shown in *Fig. 17*.

The result achieved may be explained physically on the basis of the simplified diagram in *Fig. 100*.

When coil no. 4 is disconnected, Eq. (104) assumes the form

$$V_c = \frac{C_2' i}{C_1'} + \frac{C_3' V}{C_1'}$$

i. e. the voltage V_c consists of two parts: $C_2' i / C_1'$ and $C_3' V / C_1'$ corresponding to mmf's $C_2' i$ and $C_3' V$ balancing the mmf $C_1' V_c$.

Since according to Eq. (111)

$$V - \frac{C_3'}{C_1'} V = 0$$

the component $C_3' V / C_1'$ of the voltage V_c is equalized by voltage V. Therefore only the part $C_2' i / C_1'$ acts upon winding N_c', setting up in this winding the mmf $N_c' C_2' i / C_1' r_c'$. According to the theory of the autodyne, the latter controls the current I, as in *Fig. 16*, that is

$$IN' = i_c N_c' = i \frac{C_2' N_c'}{C_1' r_c'}$$

Hence it is evident that, relying on *Fig. 98*, characteristics like $V \equiv i$ or $I \equiv i$ can easily be obtained by switching over the two coils nos. 3 and 4 of the amplidyne carrying small currents only.

Since in *Figs. 99* and *100* the mmf's $i_c N_c'$ must be equal to IN', i.e. both of them should equal also each other, the voltage $C_4' I / C_1'$ should be as high as voltage $C_2' i / C_1'$. On the other hand, the voltages $C_2' i / C_1'$ and $C_3' V / C_1'$ are equal to V and, consequently, also to each other. It follows that the voltage V_c of *Fig. 99* is the same as voltage V_c in *Fig. 100*, i. e. the amplidyne should yield the same power in both cases. The thermal load of windings N' and N_c' will be the same in both cases (as in *Fig. 16*).

CHAPTER 17

AUTODYNE WITH AUXILIARY EQUIPMENT
FOR AMPLIFYING THE SYNCHRONIZING IMPULSES

In Fig. 98 the amplidyne was used for establishing and stabilizing reference values and their components.

A (rotary or static) amplifier may also be used for other purposes, namely for amplifying the impulses transmitted by the above-mentioned feedback from the commutator of the autodyne to the mmf in the control windings, and thus ensuring the synchronization of the machine.

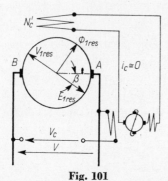

Fig. 101

An example of such a connection is shown in *Fig. 101*, where the autodyne is meant to maintain $V = V_c$, yet the voltage deviation is not connected directly to winding N_c' as in *Fig. 23*, but to the control winding of the amplidyne, creating therein mmf impulses. On the other hand, winding N_c' is connected to the armature circuit of the amplidyne and receives from this latter amplified impulses creating, in turn, amplified impulses of mmf $\mp \Delta F'$, as required by the performance of the autodyne.

In this diagram, the interdependence between mmf $\pm \Delta F'$ and the voltage variation ΔV across the brushes produced by it, does not differ from that analysed in *Chapter 6*, characterizing the autodyne. By adding a second amplification, the amplidyne only changes the feedback. The fact that the amplidyne compares the voltages V and V_c, does not interfere with the autodyne comparing two quantities. One of them is the current i_c of the amplidyne, built up by the voltage difference between V and V_c while the other is zero, i. e. the autodyne, as shown in *Fig. 23*, controls in such a way that current i_c should be zero.

It is quite natural that the amplidyne can be used also for comparing other quantities. In *Fig. 102*, for instance, a change in the control law from $V =$ constant to $I =$ constant can be ensured without the switching over of the main circuit. It differs from *Fig. 98* inasmuch as, instead of windings N_c' and N', we have only one winding N_c' supplied by the amplidyne. The principle underlying the circuit diagram of the latter in steady-state condition is the same as in *Fig. 98*,

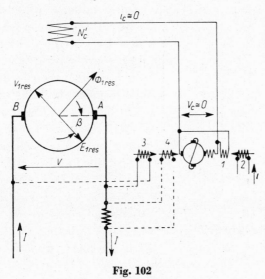

Fig. 102

with the sole difference that the directions of mmf's of coils nos. 3 and 4 are opposite to the former, and that coil no. 1 is not absolutely necessary.

According to the fundamental law of the autodyne without internal torques in steady state, the mmf and the current i_c in winding N_c' should be zero, i. e. voltage V_c and the mmf of coil no. 1 are also zero. Eq. (114) assumes the form

$$C_2' i = C_3' V + C_4' I$$

i. e. by the modification of the constants, a set of quite differently shaped load characteristics can be obtained. For instance, the two performances $V \equiv i$ and $I \equiv i$ may be achieved, as with the help of connection in *Fig. 98*. The first is obtained by switching off coil no. 4, whereby $V = C_2' i/C_3'$, the second by switching off coil no. 3, whereby $I = C_2' i/C_4'$.

Suppose now that in the autodyne a further winding is arranged, acting along any arbitrary axis and carrying an arbitrary current, e. g. winding N *(Fig. 103)* carrying current i. In this case, according to the fundamental law of the autodyne, it has to control its voltage V in such a way that current i_c in the control winding should produce a torque balancing the torque set up by current i in winding N. In this way the amplidyne will no longer keep its armature current i_c zero, but hold it at a definite value, at which the algebraic sum of the above torques in the autodyne is zero. Taking, however, into consideration that a very small deviation between V and V_c will be sufficient for building up such a current in the amplidyne armature circuit, it becomes clear that also in this case the voltage will practically be maintained at $V = V_c$.

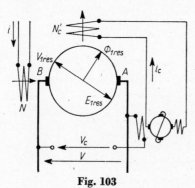

Fig. 103

In this way an autodyne, with a definite characteristic when operating independently, can be made to adopt a completely different characteristic by using for the comparison of two quantities the control coil of the rotary amplifier, feeding the control windings of the autodyne in such a way that the quantities compared by the amplifier should equal each other.

It follows also that for the circuit diagrams of *Fig. 102* and *103* the problem of accuracy and stabilization is different from that for the autodyne working together with the amplidyne according to *Fig. 98* or for autodynes according to *Figs. 23* or *16*.

An autodyne, showing whatever internal torques disturbing the state of indifferent equilibrium of $\Phi_{1r\ s}$, has to create, under all circumstances — as described in *Chapter 14* — by the aid of the mmf F_r, an electrodynamic torque compensating the internal torque. Nevertheless, the methods of creating such mmf's F_r in the above autodynes, with diverse diagrams of connections, are different.

In the autodynes of *Figs. 16, 23* and *98*, the mmf F_r is a direct consequence of the deviation between the quantities to be compared.

On the other hand, in such diagrams as those of *Figs. 102* and *103* the mmf F_r is set up by the current of the amplidyne. The ratio of this current to the deviation of the quantities to be compared is defined by the amplification factor, i. e. the gain of the amplidyne. Consequently, it is possible in principle to obtain the necessary mmf F_r at a very small deviation of controlled quantities, i. e. with a very great accuracy. Thus, in diagrams of connections, such as *Figs. 102* and *103*, the possibility arises to omit some or all methods described in *Chapters 10—13*, for eliminating internal torques, and to simplify in this way the circuit diagram of the autodyne. Here the amplidyne takes over the task of creating the necessary mmf F_r and its characteristic will determine the accuracy of the whole equipment.

It is clear that the above amplidynes can also assume the task of creating all such controlling mmf's, by the aid of which the many differently shaped characteristics described in the former chapters were obtained, or of setting up other arbitrary mmf's, varying according to diverse characteristics and created by means of small corresponding mmf's of the amplidyne.

All this refers to one of the possible types of amplifying equipments. It should be emphasized that an auxiliary autodyne may also be used to feed the control circuit (or the exciting circuit) of the main autodyne.

CHAPTER 18

SOME TRANSIENT PHENOMENA IN AN AUTODYNE CONTROLLING THE VOLTAGE

In *Chapter 6* it has been explained that the synchronizing mmf's $\pm \Delta F'$, due to the displacement of vectors $\overline{\Phi_{1\mathrm{res}}}$ and $\overline{E_{1\mathrm{res}}}$ from their steady-state situation, ensure the stabilization of the position of the said vectors.

The concomitant transient phenomena depend on the ensemble of internal and external relations, and the differential equations describing them are quite different for each diagram of connections.

A detailed theoretical analysis of these phenomena, with due consideration to all factors influencing their course, would by far exceed the limits of this book, even if we would confine ourselves to one of the above diagrams. Therefore we shall content ourselves with accounting for a few problems of practical importance involved in some of the above diagrams, neglecting terms of second order of magnitude.

For the first example we choose the diagram of *Fig. 23*.

For the time being we shall neglect the damping effect of the stator windings.

Suppose that for some reason the speed n has become greater than n_s. In this case vectors $\overline{\Phi_{1\mathrm{res}}}$ and $\overline{E_{1\mathrm{res}}}$ leave their position shown in *Fig. 104* by dotted lines, rotating with speed $n - n_s$ clockwise and

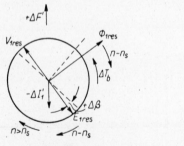

Fig. 104

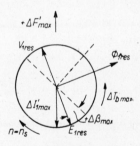

Fig. 105

covering angle $+\Delta\beta$. Consequently, owing to the above causes, a synchronizing mmf $+\Delta F'$ is set up, creating an armature current $-\Delta I_1' = -c_2\,\Delta F'$ and the corresponding braking torque T_b. This latter, owing to the inertia of the armature, does not diminish the speed instantaneously but only with a certain time lag. When n becomes equal to n_s, vectors $\overline{\Phi_{1res}}$ and $\overline{E_{1res}}$ reach their extreme positions, shown in *Fig. 105*, and quantities $+\Delta\beta$, $+\Delta F'$ and $-\Delta I_1'$ their maximum values: $+\Delta\beta_{max}$, $+\Delta F'_{max}$ and $-\Delta I'_{1max}$.

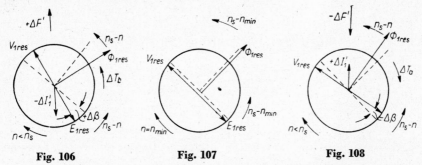

Fig. 106   Fig. 107   Fig. 108

Obviously, the braking torque ΔT_b and the deceleration of the armature reach their maximum values at this moment. In consequence, the speed of the armature will continue to decrease and be smaller than n_s.

If $n < n_s$, the vectors $\overline{\Phi_{1res}}$ and $\overline{E_{1res}}$ rotate anticlockwise with a speed $n_s - n$ *(Fig. 106)*, i. e. towards the starting position shown by dotted lines. At the same time the quantities $+\Delta\beta$, $+\Delta F'$ and $-\Delta I_1'$ as well as the braking torque ΔT_b decrease accordingly. They disappear when vectors $\overline{\Phi_{1res}}$ and $\overline{E_{1res}}$ reach their starting positions *(Fig. 107)*. Meanwhile the braking torque had decreased the speed n until n_{min}. Consequently, vectors $\overline{\Phi_{1res}}$ and $\overline{E_{1res}}$ will pass through their starting positions with speed $n_s - n_{min}$ and keep rotating with speed $n_s - n$ anticlockwise *(Fig. 108)*. Hence $\Delta\beta$, $\Delta F'$ and $\Delta I_1'$ thein change sign, thus creating an accelerating torque ΔT_a. Owing to inertia, the latter cannot increase n again to n_s, until vectors $\overline{\Phi_{1res}}$ and $\overline{E_{1res}}$ have reached their extreme positions *(Fig. 109)* and the quantities $-\Delta\beta$, $-\Delta F'$, and $+\Delta I_1'$ their extreme values $-\Delta\beta_{max}$, $-\Delta F'_{max}$ and $+\Delta I'_{1max}$. The accelerating torque meanwhile also reaches its maximum value ΔT_{amax} and forces n to enlarge. Consequently, vectors $\overline{\Phi_{1r\,s}}$ and $\overline{E_{1res}}$ rotate again clockwise with speed $n - n_s$ *(Fig.*

10*

110), whereby $-\Delta\beta$, $-\Delta F'$ and $+\Delta I'_1$ decrease until zero *(Fig. 111)*, when vectors $\overline{\Phi_{1res}}$ and $\overline{E_{1res}}$ pass through their starting position. Hence n increases until n_{max} and, owing to the inertia of the armature, vectors $\overline{\Phi_{1res}}$ and $\overline{E_{1res}}$ go on rotating clockwise with speed $n - n_s$ as shown in *Fig. 104*. Thus undamped oscillations of vectors $\overline{\Phi_{1res}}$ and $\overline{E_{1res}}$ arise within the extreme positions shown in *Figs. 105* and *109*.

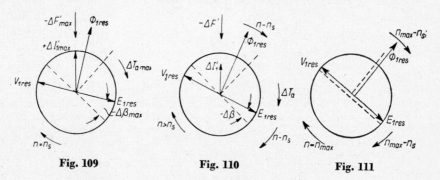

Fig. 109   Fig. 110   Fig. 111

Let us investigate now, what influence the short-circuited stator windings, e. g., the excitation windings, and the friction-compensating windings will exert on the character of transient phenomena.

Obviously, these windings will have the same influence as the damping windings in synchronous machines, i. e. will set up torques tending to counteract the deviation of the rotor from synchronous speed. Under the influence of these torques, the above-mentioned oscillations of the rotor will soon be damped.

The transient phenomena, as influenced by such stator windings, are illustrated in *Figs. 112—114*.

In *Fig. 107*, vector $\overline{\Phi_{1res}}$ passes through its starting position and rotates with maximum speed $n_s - n_{min}$ anticlockwise. This

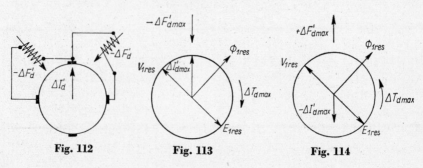

Fig. 112   Fig. 113   Fig. 114

means that at the given instant the direct-axis component $\overline{\Phi'_1}$ of flux $\overline{\Phi_{1res}}$ and flux Φ' increase with maximum velocity and thus the induced voltage in the turns of the stator windings linked with Φ' have the maximum value. This voltage builds up the mmf's $-\Delta F'_d$ *(Fig. 112)*. By neglecting the reactance of the stator windings, on account of the relatively low frequency of these oscillations, the mmf's $-\Delta F'_d$ will have at this moment their maximum value $-\Delta F'_{dmax}$, and the total mmf will have the direction as shown in *Fig. 113*. Thus the compensating current $\Delta I'_d$ *(Fig. 112)*, created by these mmf's and acting in the opposite direction, will also have its maximum value $\Delta I'_{dmax}$ *(Fig. 113)* and produce a motor power and a corresponding accelerating torque ΔT_{dmax}, counteracting the oscillations of the armature, and therefore representing a damping torque.

In a position corresponding to *Fig. 111 (Fig. 114)* damping mmf's $+\Delta F'_{dmax}$ and a damping torque ΔT_{dmax} arise, counteracting the oscillations of the armature. It is easy to understand that the mmf $\mp\Delta F'_d$ *(Figs. 113 and 114)*, causing the oscillations to decay, is leading with respect to the synchronizing mmfs $\mp\Delta F'$, provoking the oscillations of flux $\overline{\Phi_{1res}}$ around its starting position.

The above only holds if, beside the flux Φ' inducing the emf E in the armature, no other fluxes are present along the direct axis of the machine. In fact, we have hitherto started from the assumption that the mmf's produced by the compensating currents in the armature totally eliminate the mmf's in the stator provoking them.

In reality, however, the following conditions have to be taken into consideration:

1. According to the theory of compensating currents expounded in *Chapter 4*, the emf, induced in the phase windings of the armature by the flux due to the mmf $+\Delta F'$, is equal and opposite to the emf induced by the flux due to the mmf of the compensating current $-\Delta I'_1$. Since the emf in the phase windings is induced practically by the fundamental of the flux only, the fundamental waves of the flux produced by mmf $\Delta F'$ and the flux produced by mmf due to current $-\Delta I'_1$ have to be equal to each other.

By taking into consideration that mmf $+\Delta F'$ *(Fig. 104)* is produced by windings (e. g. N' in *Fig. 16*) arranged on half poles, the flux produced by mmf's in the half poles will be found to be distributed along the circumference of the armature, according to a curve containing harmonics, e.g., in the configuration of *Fig. 59* as shown by the line $1-2-3-4-5-6-7-8$ *(Fig. 115)*. The mmf produced by current $-\Delta I_1'$ *(Fig. 104)* is distributed, in turn, sinusoidally, but the flux set up by it (in the same configuration), according to the line $1-9-10-4-5-11-12-8$ *(Fig. 115)*. In order to obtain equal fundamentals for both distributions of the flux, the fundamental waves of areas $13-9-2-13-3-10$ and $14-6-11-14-12-7$ should equal zero. This is only possible if the areas $13-3-10$ and $14-6-11$, situated nearer to the symmetry axis, are smaller than the areas $13-9-2$ and $14-12-7$. This means that the flux produced by mmf $+\Delta F'$ will be somewhat greater than the flux due to compensating current $-\Delta I_1'$. In other words, at the instant corresponding to *Fig. 105*, when $\overline{\Phi_{1\mathrm{res}}}$ is in its extreme position, beside the downward change in flux $\Phi'_{\max}$, a very small residual flux is obtained with the direction $+\Delta F'_{\max}$, i. e. opposite to the variation of flux $\Phi'_{\max}$.

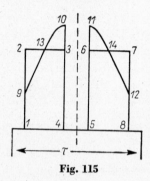

Fig. 115

2. The assumption that the emf induced in the phase winding by the flux set up by the mmf due to current $-\Delta I_1'$ is equal to the emf induced by the flux set up by $+\Delta F'$, would hold good only if the phase winding had no resistance. The resistance can indeed be neglected. But since the phase windings, i. e. the armature circuit, has a reactance due to the leakage flux, the emf generated by $+\Delta F'$ will be compensated not only by the emf generated owing to current $-\Delta I_1'$, but also by the inductive voltage drop produced by the latter. Hence the current $-\Delta I_1'$ will in reality decrease by a still smaller value than assumed in point 1, causing a further increment of the residual flux mentioned in this point and a decrement of the damping action of flux Φ'.

3. The leakage flux set up by the mmf $\Delta F'$ in the stator also induces, by the changes in its quantity and direction, certain emfs in the stator windings, amplifying the phenomena described in points 1 and 2 and further diminishing mmf $\Delta F_d'$ and the damping torque ΔT_d.

Beside flux Φ' proportional to Φ_1', flux Φ proportional to Φ_1 also exerts a damping effect. It will be shown that the residual damping action of both fluxes Φ and Φ' is a given quantity at certain parameters of the winding system for slip excitation and of the winding system for compensating the frictional torque (cf. Eq. 115c). On the other hand, it is clear that the stronger the phenomena listed in points 1—3 act, the greater the ratio $\Delta F'/\Delta\beta$, i. e. the synchronizing mmf per unit of angle deviation. This ratio will henceforth be termed *specific synchronizing mmf*. It follows that there is a definite specific synchronizing mmf $\Delta F'/\Delta\beta$ (and a great one, at that), at which the actual diminished value of the damping torque ΔT_{dd} decreases until zero, i. e. at which undamped oscillations arise. At still greater values of $\Delta F'/\Delta\beta$, torque ΔT_{dd} is obviously opposed to the former, i. e. the torque will, instead of attenuating further, amplify the oscillations of flux $\overline{\Phi_{1res}}$.

The quantitative side of this question can be elucidated by the following considerations.

The increment of angle β by $\Delta\beta$ diminishes the direct-axis component $\Phi_{1res}\cos\beta$ of flux $\overline{\Phi_{1res}}$ by $-\Phi_{1res}\sin\beta\,\Delta\beta$. Thereby mmf's $+\Delta F'_d$ are produced proportional to the change in flux, i. e.

$$\Delta F'_d = - A_1\,\Phi_{1res}\sin\beta\,\Delta\beta \tag{114}$$

and a braking torque arises

$$\Delta T_{d1} \cong A_2\,\Delta F'_d\,\Phi_{1res}\sin\beta = - A_2\,A_1\,\Phi^2_{1res}\sin^2\beta\,\Delta\beta \tag{115a}$$

where A_1 and A_2 are proportionality constants. Obviously, at the same time, by increasing the quadrature-axis component $\Phi_{1res}\sin\beta$ of flux $\overline{\Phi_{1res}}$ by $\Phi_{1res}\cos\beta\,\Delta\beta$ a second component of damping torque

$$\Delta T_{d2} \cong - A_2\,A_1\,\Phi^2_{1res}\cos^2\beta\,\Delta\beta \tag{115b}$$

arises. Hence

$$\Delta T_d = \Delta T_{d1} + \Delta T_{d2} \cong - A_2\,A_1\,\Phi_{1res}\,\Delta\beta \tag{115c}$$

On the other hand, an increase of angle β by $\Delta\beta$ creates a definite synchronizing mmf $+\Delta F'$. The relation between $+\Delta\beta$ and $+\Delta F'$ may be determined with sufficient accuracy on the basis of the following consideration: if the situation of vector $\overline{V_{1res}}$ changes by $-\Delta\beta$, its horizontal component $V_{1res}\cos\beta$ diminishes by $-V_{1res}\sin\beta\,\Delta\beta$. At the same time, the value of voltage V across the brushes diminishes by the value

$$\Delta V = - c_1 V_{1\mathrm{res}} \sin \beta \, \Delta \beta$$

(the autodyne is assumed to operate at no load).

In case of *Fig. 23*

$$+ \Delta F' = - \frac{\Delta V}{r_c'} N_c' \tag{116}$$

In this case the specific synchronizing mmf is

$$\frac{\Delta F'}{\Delta \beta} = \frac{N_c'}{r_c'} c_1 V_{1\mathrm{res}} \sin \beta \tag{117}$$

Finally, as stated above, for reasons listed in points $1-3$, a certain part of the specific synchronizing mmf $\Delta F'/\Delta \beta$ diminishes the changes in flux $\Phi_{1\mathrm{res}}$ as well as the quantities $\Delta F_d'/\Delta \beta$ by $A_3 \Delta F'/\Delta \beta$ and $\Delta T_{d1}/\Delta \beta$ (cf. Eq. 115a) by $A_3 A_2 \Delta F' \, \Phi_{1\mathrm{res}} \sin \beta/\Delta \beta$, where A_3 is a proportionality factor.

Thus the actual diminished damping torque is

$$\Delta T_{dd} = A_2 A_1 \Phi_{1\mathrm{res}}^2 \Delta \beta - A_2 A_3 \frac{N_c'}{r_c'} c_1 V_{1\mathrm{res}} \Phi_{1\mathrm{res}} \sin^2 \beta \, \Delta \beta =$$

$$= A_2 A_4 V_{1\mathrm{res}}^2 \left(A_1 A_4 - \sin^2 \beta \, A_3 c_1 \frac{N_c'}{r_c'} \right) \Delta \beta \tag{118}$$

where

$$A_4 = \frac{\Phi_{1\mathrm{res}}}{V_{1\mathrm{res}}} \tag{119}$$

is practically constant.

The resistance per turn of the control winding r_c'/N_c' has a value — as shown in *Chapter 14* (see Eq. 87) — which, expressed in percentages, is proportional to the inaccuracy of control, i. e. to the relative voltage deviation for autodynes maintaining $V = V_c$.

As tests with the AB type autodynes and theoretical calculations have shown, even for small values of r_c'/N_c' at which the inaccuracy of control amounts only to $1-2$ per cent, the quantity $c_1 A_3 N_c'/r_c'$ is much smaller than $A_1 A_4$. Consequently, ΔT_{dd} has a positive value, is high enough, and the machine thus does not require any supplementary means for maintaining its stability.

Fig. 116 shows oscillograms of the voltage V prevailing between the brushes and of the changes in the control current i_c for the A—3B type autodyne in case of reversing the control voltage V_c.

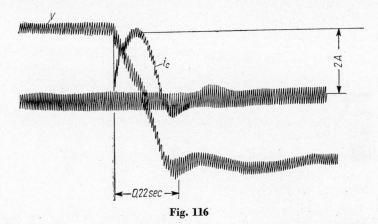

Fig. 116

This oscillogram shows that, at sudden changes of the voltage from $+V_{rated}$ to $-V_{rated}$, the operation of the machine is quite stable. The change of voltage within the limits shown takes 0·22 sec, that is, the mean velocity of voltage change is about 2100 V/sec.

CHAPTER 19

SOME PARTICULARITIES OF TRANSIENT PHENOMENA IN AN AUTODYNE STABILIZING THE CHARGING CURRENT OF BATTERIES

In case of *Fig. 16*, the deviation ΔV from V changes the current I by ΔI which, by neglecting the inductive reactance in the main circuit, may be calculated on the basis of the following considerations.

According to Eq. (93)

$$V = c_1 V_{1res} \cos \beta - (c_1 b + a) I$$

The voltage drop in winding N', caused by current I, is $I r_{N'}$ where $r_{N'}$ is the resistance of the winding. By denoting the resistance of the brushes by r_B, the resistance of the series quadrature-axis coil in *Fig. 78a* by r_F, the resistance of the series-connected commutating poles by r_C, the resistance of the load circuit by R_L, and the internal voltage (or emf) of the battery by E_B, we obtain the equation

$$c_1 V_{1res} \cos \beta - (c_1 b + a) I = I(r_{N'} + r_B + r_F + r_C + R_L) + E_B \quad \text{(120a)}$$

When angle β changes by $\Delta \beta$, the voltage component $c_1 V_{1res} \cos \beta$ changes by $c_1 V_{1res} \sin \beta \, \Delta \beta$, and I by ΔI, while E_B remains unchanged.

By neglecting the influence of self-inductance as before, we obtain

$$c_1 V_{1res} \sin \beta \, \Delta \beta = \Delta I(c_1 b + a + r_{N'} + r_B + r_F + r_C + R_L) \quad \text{(120b)}$$

Let us denote

$$c_1 b + a + r_{N'} + r_B + r_F + r_C = \Sigma R_a \quad \text{(121)}$$

where ΣR_a is the resulting internal resistance of the autodyne with regard to the voltage drop in the phase winding too, caused by the alternating current I_1 proportional to 1 *(Chapter 14)*.

As a result we obtain for the mmf impulse in winding N'

$$\Delta F' = \Delta I N' = \frac{N' c_1 V_{1res} \sin \beta \, \Delta \beta}{\Sigma R_a + R_L} \tag{122}$$

Instead of N'_c/r'_c (see Eq. (118)), a decisive factor, as explained in *Chapter 18*, for stability of the autodyne of *Fig. 23*, we have now the term

$$\frac{N'}{\Sigma R_a + R_L}$$

determining the stability of the autodyne of *Figs. 16* and *18*.

In the machine of *Fig. 16* the stability will be the greater, the higher the resistance R_L and the less the number of turns N' is.

This has been checked by test results.

In an autodyne operating according to *Fig. 18* in connection with a storage battery, the external resistance R_L can be neglected at the first approximation. On the other hand, the resistance of the windings carrying current I and I_1 with a great cross section, is very low. Therefore the ratio $\Sigma R_a/N'$ is relatively small and, consequently, the quantity

$$\frac{\sin^2 \beta \, A_3 c_1 N'}{\Sigma R_a}$$

to be substituted in Eq. (118) may, under certain circumstances, be greater than $A_1 A_4$ and therefore ΔT_{dd} will have negative values. Hence the autodyne of *Fig. 18* might re-
quire, under certain circumstances, supplementary means for ensuring the stability. This means consists in arranging a damping winding on the half poles in form of an 8-shaped double loop *(Fig. 117)*. This was pro-posed by the author on the strength of the following considerations:

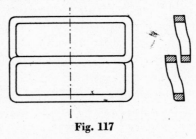

Fig. 117

Suppose that the vectors of flux $\overline{\Phi_{1res}}$ and of the emf $\overline{E_{1res}}$ are in one of the extreme positions, as shown in *Figs. 105* and *109*. Then an mmf $\Delta F'_{max}$ and a current $\Delta I'_{1max}$ compensating it arises. In the autodyne here investigated

$$\Delta F'_{max} = \Delta I_{max} N' \qquad (123)$$

$$\Delta I'_{1max} = c_2 \Delta I_{max} N' \qquad (124)$$

In this case fluxes arise corresponding to the areas 9—2—13—3—10—13 and 6—11—14—12—7—14 *(Fig. 115).*

Let us now investigate the distribution of these fluxes.

The fluxes corresponding to the areas 2—9—13 and 12—7—14 have, obviously, the same direction as fluxes set up by mmf $\Delta F'$, corresponding to areas 1—2—3—4 and 5—6—7—8. The fluxes corresponding to areas 3—13—10 and 6—14—11 have an opposite direction, i. e. the same as the mmf produced by current $-\Delta I'_1$. The flux corresponding to the area 9—13—2 may be regarded as composed of the fluxes coinciding in direction and complying with areas 2—13'—9' and

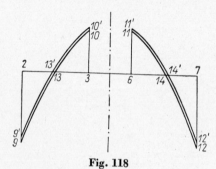

Fig. 118

9—9'—13'—13 *(Fig. 118).* The flux corresponding to the area 13—3—10 may be conceived as composed of the flux of area 13'—3—10', having the direction of the mmf produced by current $-\Delta I'_1$ and the opposite flux complying with area 13—13'—10'—10, whereby the fluxes corresponding to areas 2—13'—9' and 13'—3—10' are equal in magnitude. The flux corresponding to area 6—11—14—12—7—14 can be treated analogously. The actual flux arising on common action of mmf $\Delta F'$ and of the mmf produced by current $-\Delta I'_1$, may be considered to be composed of two fluxes:

The one corresponding to areas 9—9'—13'—10'—10—13—9 and 11—11'—14'—12'—12—14—11 has the direction of mmf $\Delta F'$ and represents a residual flux. It passes, obviously, along the same magnetic paths as the fluxes corresponding to areas 1—2—3—4 and 5—6—7—8 *(Fig. 115)* or flux Φ' to which it is opposed.

The second flux also consists of two fluxes. One of them corresponds to area 9'—2—13'—3—10', the other to area 6—11'—14'—12'—7, i. e. these fluxes close within the half poles *(Fig. 119).* They can therefore produce no voltages in the ordinary stator windings and do not act upon the fluxes corresponding to areas 9—9'—13'—10'—

10—13—9 and 11—14—12—12′—14′—11′—11 *(Fig. 118)* and are, therefore, distributed uniformly along the air gap.

On the other hand, we obtain quite another picture by arranging conductors in the form of double loops according to *Fig. 117*, linked with the said fluxes *(Fig. 119)*, in order that the changes in the latter could produce voltages in the double loops.

Let us investigate this process in greater detail.

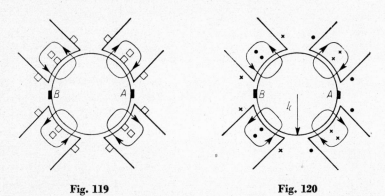

Fig. 119   Fig. 120

When flux $\overline{\Phi_{1\text{res}}}$ passes with maximum velocity through the position represented in *Fig. 111*, the quantities $\Delta F'$, ΔI_1 and the fluxes illustrated in *Fig. 119* pass through zero. The emf induced in this moment by this latter in the said circuits will reach its maximum value.

The current created by this emf will also reach its maximum if in first approximation the reactance of the circuit is neglected. Its direction and the direction of the fluxes produced by it are shown in *Fig. 120*. The distribution of these fluxes along the upper half of the armature circumference is shown in *Fig. 121*. Here the negative areas 1—2—3—4 and 5—6—7—8 comply with the entering fluxes *(Fig. 120)* and the areas 4—9—10—11 and 12—13—14—5 comply with the fluxes leaving the armature. Since the algebraic sum of these areas is zero, i. e. the arising fluxes close entirely within the half poles, they cannot induce any d-c emf between brushes A and B. The fundamental wave of the flux distribution, however, corresponding to areas 4—9—10—11 and 12—13—14—5 *(Fig. 121)* is, on account of these areas lying close to the symmetry axis, greater than the fundamental wave complying with areas 1—2—3—4 and 5—6—7—8.

Therefore the algebraic sum of the fundamental waves (curve 15—16—17) sets up in the armature a compensating current I_C the direction of which is marked by an arrow *(Fig. 120)*. This current, like current $-\Delta I'_{dmax}$ *(Fig. 114)*, produces with the emf E_{1res}, a generator power responsible for a damping torque.

Owing to the minuteness of the algebraic sum of fundamental waves, the magnitudes of the compensating current I_C *(Fig. 120)* and

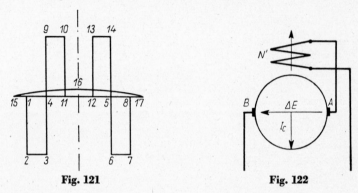

Fig. 121   Fig. 122

of the supplementary braking torque appear, at the first glance, unimportant.

While, at the same time, the emf induced in the phase winding by the flux of the compensating current, practically compensates the emf induced in the same winding by the entire flux of the fundamental wave *(Fig. 121)*, the emf induced in the d-c circuit between brushes A and B by the compensating current is not cancelled by the influence of the flux shown in *Fig. 120*, because this latter creates no emf between brushes A and B. In this way the only emf prevailing between these brushes is the emf ΔE, induced by the compensating current and directed in the quadrature axis from right to left *(Fig. 122)*. It builds up a current passing also through the series winding N' and produces with it an upward mmf. This creates a downward compensating current and in this way amplifies the original compensating current. In consequence, the whole process described above of the development of emf ΔE is further enhanced. Calculations show that the supplementary damping torque achieved in this way is very great. It should be noted that the flux shown in *Fig. 119* grows with the magnification of $\Delta F'$ and $\Delta I'_1$. The damping torque obtained in this way increases therefore with the growth of mmf $\Delta F'$, i. e. of the value $N'/\Sigma R_a$, contrary to the one created by means of other stator windings. This means that in Eq. (118) we shall have, instead of the constant quantities $A_1 A_4$, a quantity $A_6 N'/\Sigma R_a$ within the brackets, where A_6 is a constant. If the far greater value $N'/\Sigma R_a$ is substituted for N'_c/r'_c, the damping torque component ΔT_{dd} may still preserve its positive sign. This accounts for the considerable stability of the autodyne of *Fig. 16,* even at a sudden transition from no load to total short circuit.

CHAPTER 20

THE STABILITY OF THE AUTODYNE
WITH AN AUXILIARY AMPLIDYNE

As far as the synchronizing mmf created by the change $\Delta\beta$ in angle β is concerned, the circuit diagram of the autodyne in *Fig. 98* does not differ in principle from the diagram of *Figs. 16* or *23*. If angle β and the voltage V change adequately, the same synchronizing mmf's

$$\frac{\Delta V N_c'}{r_c'} \quad \text{and} \quad \frac{\Delta V N'}{\Sigma R_a + R_L}$$

arise immediately and simultaneously in *Fig. 98* as in *Figs. 23* and *16*.

It is, however, necessary to take into consideration the following circumstance: if coil no. 3 *(Fig. 98)* is disconnected and coil no. 4 inserted, i. e. S_1 and S_2 are in position b, the autodyne maintains the voltage V constant. The mmf IN' is then cancelled by the mmf $i_c N_c'$, produced by that part $C_4'I/C_1'$ of V_c, which is set up by the mmf of winding no. 4. If the angle β and therefore also the voltage V alter, also I and IN' will change. Yet at the same time the mmf in coil no. 4, the corresponding part $C_4'I/C_1'$ of V_c *(Fig. 99)* and the mmf $i_c N_c'$ created by it, also change in the same ratio but opposite to the change in mmf IN'. Consequently, if the autodyne keeps the voltage constant as in *Fig. 98*, no mmf is created by the change in current I and only such synchronizing mmf's

$$\Delta F' = \frac{N_c'}{r_c'} c_1 V_{1\text{res}} \sin\beta \, \Delta\beta$$

are in action as arise in the machine according to *Fig. 23*.

But if coil no. 4 *(Fig. 98)* is disconnected and coil no. 3 is inserted, i. e. S_1 and S_2 are in position a, then the autodyne holds the current I constant. Here voltage V balances that part $C_3'V/C_1'$ *(Fig. 100)* of V_c, which corresponds to the mmf in coil no. 3. Consequently, only that part of voltage V_c acts on winding N_c', which corresponds to the mmf produced by current i, flowing in coil no. 2. If the angle β varies and therefore also the voltage V changes by $\pm \Delta V$, the mmf in coil no. 3 and the corresponding part $C_3' V / C_1'$ of V_c also changes in ratio $\Delta V / V$. This variation is obviously equal and opposite to the variation of voltage V. Hence when the autodyne maintains the current constant according to *Fig. 98*, no mmf is set up by voltage variations and only such synchronizing mmf's

$$\Delta F' = \frac{N'}{R + \Sigma R_a} c_1 V_{1\mathrm{res}} \sin \beta \ \Delta \beta$$

are present as also arise in the machine according to *Fig. 16*.

It is easy to understand that any change in the direct-axis component Φ_1' of flux $\overline{\Phi_{1\mathrm{res}}}$ in the machine of *Fig. 98*, creates the same damping mmf's $\Delta F_d'$ and damping torques ΔT_d, as in the ordinary autodynes. Moreover it is clear also that the above-listed causes, diminishing ΔT_{dd} and changing its sign, act in this machine as much as in ordinary autodynes.

In the autodyne of *Fig. 98*, however, there is an additional possibility for ensuring the stability of the machine without using double-loop windings, even at very great values of specific synchonizing mmf's $\Delta F' / \Delta \beta$, at which the damping torque component ΔT_{dd} obtained in the way described above, is already zero.

Here we may start from certain assumptions which, naturally, can represent, only with a very rough approximation, the phenomena occurring in reality, the particularities of which could be clarified only by the analytical investigation of the transient phenomena.

As shown above, the damping mmf's $\Delta F_d'$ are leading with respect to the synchronizing mmf's $\Delta F'$. Hence supplementary damping torques may be obtained by creating oscillations of voltage V, producing in winding N_c' leading mmf's $\Delta F'$. This may be realized in different ways.

Suppose, for instance, that the autodyne holds current I constant, for which purpose winding no. 3 *(Fig. 98)* is connected to voltage V, while winding no. 4 is disconnected from the circuit carrying current I. It is, however, connected through switch S_2 to the secondary winding of transformer T_2. In this way, when the current I in the primary winding changes by $\pm \Delta I$, voltages are induced in the secondary winding, proportional to ΔI and building up an alternating current in coil no. 4. Should this coincide in phase with current

$\pm \Delta I$, such oscillations of mmf $i_c N_c'$ could obviously be obtained by means of the amplidyne, as are opposed to the oscillations of $\pm \Delta I\ N'$ in winding N', i. e. leading by 180°. If, however, the current in coil no. 4 is made to lag behind current ΔI, then at least a certain part of the current in coil no. 4 will establish such oscillations of mmf in winding N_c', which are leading with respect to the synchronizing mmfs $\pm \Delta I\ N'$, and result in supplementary damping torques.

Since these torques and the leading mmfs provoking them are proportional to the synchronizing mmf's $\pm \Delta I\ N'$, it will become clear that the value of the specific synchronizing mmf $\pm \Delta I\ N'/\Delta \beta$ according to *Fig. 98* can be enlarged without impairing stability.

Similar considerations show it to be expedient, in the autodyne maintaining V constant, to connect coil no. 3 to the secondary winding of transformer T_1 (position b of switch S_1), the primary winding of which is supplied through a series resistance R by voltage V. Consequently, any voltage change $\pm \Delta V$ creates in the secondary winding a corresponding mmf which, in turn, builds up an alternating current in coil no. 3. Should this coincide in phase with voltage ΔV, then such oscillations of mmf $i_c N_c'$ could, obviously, be achieved by means of the amplidyne, as are opposed to the oscillations of mmf $i_c N_c'$, created directly by the change in voltage ΔV, i. e. are leading by 180°.

If the current in coil no. 3 can be made to lag behind ΔV, then at least a certain part of the mmf of winding no. 3 will create by the aid of the amplidyne, such mmf's in winding N_c' as are leading with respect to the synchronizing mmf

$$\pm \Delta F' = \frac{N_c'}{r_c'} c_1 V_{1res} \sin \beta\ \Delta \beta$$

and thereby producing supplementary damping torques.

Since these torques and the leading mmf's provoking them are proportional to the synchronizing mmf's $\pm \Delta F'$, the value of specific synchronizing mmf $\pm \Delta F'/\Delta \beta$ according to *Fig. 98* can be increased without diminishing stability.

On the other hand, it is clear that the increase of values $\Delta I\ N'/\Delta \beta$ and $\Delta F'/\Delta \beta$, i. e. of the synchronizing torque, referred to unit angle deviation, enhances the acceleration or deceleration of the armature, whereby the time necessary for the changes ΔV or ΔI is diminished accordingly.

The greater the values $\Delta I\, N'/\Delta\beta$ and $\Delta F'/\Delta\beta$, the greater the stability of the current I and the voltage V.

In reality, the maximum value $\Delta F'$ is

$$\frac{V_{\max}\,\Delta\beta\,N_c'}{r_c'}$$

Since $V_{\max} = V_{c\max}$, the mmf $V_{c\max}N_c'/r_c'$ in Eq. (87) will be greater, the greater $\Delta F'/\Delta\beta$ is, i. e. the degree of accuracy grows proportionally to the value of $\Delta F'/\Delta\beta$.

Fig. 102 differs in principle from *Fig. 98* in the process of ensuring the synchronous run of the autodyne. In *Fig. 98* the synchronizing mmf's $\pm\Delta F'$ are produced directly in the autodyne by the effect of voltages $\pm\Delta V$ upon the winding N_c' or by that of the current ΔI in the circuit of winding N'. The action of the amplidyne refers chiefly to the steady state, as its task is to create a steady-state voltage V_c intended, on the one hand, to establish a reference value and, on the other, to eliminate the undesired mmf's.

The amplidyne in this system transmits and amplifies the quantitites ΔI *(Fig. 99)* and ΔV *(Fig. 100)* as well, but its effect is only meant to cancel the undesired mmf's in the autodyne. Therefore, the amplidyne really takes no part in producing the mmf's $\Delta F'$ acting as synchronizing mmf impulses in the autodyne.

Fig. 102 yields an entirely different picture. Here the autodyne sets up no synchronizing mmf's, since the changes in voltage V and current I cannot effect the creation of the mmf's in winding N_c'. The impulses of the mmf $\pm\Delta F'$ in winding N_c' are created only by the appearance of impulses $\pm\Delta V_c$ between the terminals of the amplidyne. These are due to the sum of the mmf's in coils nos. 1, 2, 3, 4 being not zero, i. e. to the effect the quantities $\pm\Delta V$ and $\pm\Delta I$ have upon coils nos. 3 and 4. In this case the amplidyne may be said to be a synchronizing one, while in case of *Fig. 98* the amplidyne fulfils chiefly purposes of control.

From the above it may be concluded that by transmitting the synchronizing impulses through the cascade of electric and magnetic circuits (coils nos. 3 or 4, direct-axis flux of the amplidyne, quadrature-axis circuit and flux of the amplidyne, circuit of winding N_c' *(Fig. 102)*), the characteristic equation appearing will be of a higher order than in the case of a direct transmission of impulses ΔV or ΔI to windings N_c' or N' according to *Fig. 98*.

11*

As stated above, the lag of the changes in the mmf's of coils nos. 3 and 4 *(Fig. 102)* behind the impulses ΔV or ΔI provoking them, acts in a direction to diminish the torques ΔT_{dd}. On the other hand, similar changes in the same mmf's as shown in *Fig. 98* will act in a direction to amplifying these torques, since the direction of mmf's of coils nos. 3 and 4 in this connection is opposite to the direction of the same mmf's in *Fig. 102*. Therefore the steady-state operation of the autodyne of *Fig. 102* should be ensured by employing the usual methods to make the impulses of mmf in coils nos. 3 and 4 lead.

CHAPTER 21

THE RESPONSE SPEED OF THE AUTODYNE

As explained in *Chapter 1,* an autodyne can not only be used in place of a motor generator but represents at the same time a new control type machine. It was also mentioned that, when operating as a rotary amplifier, the advantages of the autodyne are the absence of the driving motor and the ineffectiveness of sudden change in load upon speed, etc. Comparing the autodyne with the amplidyne, the latter is on the margin of self-excitation, when the demagnetizing effect of the armature reaction is entirely compensated in the direct axis.

In the autodyne this problem does not occur, because amplification can take place in the direct axis, while the armature reaction acts in the quadrature axis. In this respect certain difficulties encountered in the construction of high-capacity amplidynes do not occur in the case of autodynes. Meanwhile a problem of great importance for the use of autodynes instead of amplidynes requires deeper analysis. This is the mechanical inertia of the rotor as a factor counteracting the response speed of the autodyne.

In control type machines developed on the basis of d-c generators (*Fig. 7b.*), a magnetic flux and a voltage are in fact created in the exciting circuit immediately after the appearance of the mmf impulse (if the effect of eddy currents is neglected). This voltage builds up a current comparatively soon and a flux changing the output voltage. In the autodyne, however, the mmf impulses act by means of torques provoked by them, accelerating or decelerating the armature to enable flux $\overline{\Phi}_{1\mathrm{res}}$ to turn to a new position. The qualitative investigation of factors acting on the response speed of the autodyne, e.g., on the speed of the variation of parameter Π_1 at a sudden change of parameter Π_2, is even more intricate than that of stability, since it requires a thorough analysis of transient phenomena.

It is, however, possible to make a number of fundamental statements for the simplest autodynes, as shown, for instance, in *Figs. 16* and *23*, yielding a certain basis for a qualitative comparison of the response speed of the autodyne and the other control type machines constructed on the basis of d-c generators.

Suppose that the autodyne *(Fig. 23)* operates at a small voltage $V = V_c$. If V_c diminishes the speed to zero, consequently, the position of flux $\overline{\Phi_{1\mathrm{res}}}$ and also the armature voltage V remain

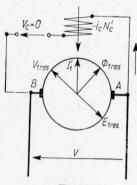

Fig. 123

unchanged in the first moment. Hence the control winding is practically connected to voltage V. The latter then builds up the current i_c and the downward mmf $-i_c N'_c$ *(Fig. 123)*, which in turn produces the compensating current $+I'_1$ directed upward.

Should the mmf $i_c N'_c$ be distributed sinusoidally along the circumference and should there be no leakage fluxes linked with the phase winding of the rotor or with the control winding, then the emf of mutual induction created in winding N'_c by current I'_1 would cancel the entire emf of self-induction caused in the same winding i_c. In reality, however (as stated in *Chapter 18*), the non-sinusoidal distribution of mmf $i_c N'_c$ and the presence of leakage fluxes linked with the armature winding and with control winding N'_c, respectively, create a self-induction emf having but a few per cent value of the emf produced by mmf $i_c N'_c$.

Hence, unlike the exciting and control circuits of control type machines built on the basis of d-c generators or transductors, any change of control current in the autodyne causes an incomparably smaller emf of self-induction and is therefore markedly further ahead than in the machines mentioned.

This can be seen clearly in the oscillogram of *Fig. 116*, in which the control current i_c grows up to the maximum value within a tenth of a second, although the voltage $V_c - V$ building up this current falls meanwhile to half of its value.

It may be concluded that, while in the control type machines enumerated above, the response speed is primarily in connection with magnetic inertia, in the autodyne it is related to the mechanical inertia of the armature.

By neglecting the influence of leakage fluxes and higher harmonics of mmf $i_c N_c'$, we find the current in the control winding to increase suddenly to

$$i_c = \frac{V}{r_c'} \tag{125a}$$

and the mmf to

$$- F' = \frac{V N_c'}{r_c'} \tag{125b}$$

Obviously, the acceleration of the armature, due to mmf F', will be proportional to this latter and inversely proportional to the moment of inertia of the armature J. The compensating current I_1' has the value

$$I_1' \simeq - \frac{F'}{N_{\text{eff}}} \tag{126}$$

where N_{eff} is the effective number of turns of the three-phase winding on the armature, consisting of a parallel circuits.

The flux $\Phi_{1\text{res}}$ per pair of poles p induces in the same turns the emf

$$E_{1\text{res}} = C \Phi_{1\text{res}} N_{\text{eff}} \frac{pn}{60} \tag{127}$$

where C is a constant. The power produced by the total current $a I_1'$ is

$$P = 3 E_{1\text{res}} a I_1' = 3 C \Phi_{1\text{res}} a F' \frac{pn}{60} \tag{128}$$

By assuming $p = a$ we obtain for the corresponding torque

$$T = \frac{30 P}{\pi n} = \frac{3}{2 \pi} C \Phi_{1\text{res}} F' p^2 \tag{129}$$

The initial angular acceleration of the armature will be

$$\frac{T}{J} = \frac{3 C \Phi_{1\text{res}} F' p^2}{2 \pi J} \tag{130}$$

By denoting

$$90 - \beta = \varepsilon \tag{131}$$

and assuming, for the sake of simplicity, quantity V to be so small, that during the transient phenomena

$$V = c_1 V_{1res} \cos \beta = c_1 V_{1res} \sin \varepsilon \cong c_1 V_{1res} \varepsilon \qquad (132)$$

By neglecting the influence of damping, and considering Eqs. (125b), (130) and (132), we obtain for the acceleration of the armature caused by mmf $- F'$

$$\frac{T}{J} = \frac{3 C c_1 \Phi_{1res} p^2 N_c' V_{1res} \varepsilon}{2 \pi J r_c'} \qquad (133)$$

where ε is expressed in radians.

On the other hand, the angular acceleration of the armature is

$$\frac{T}{J} = \frac{1}{p} \frac{d^2\beta}{dt^2} = -\frac{1}{p} \frac{d^2\varepsilon}{dt^2} \qquad (134)$$

By substituting T/J from Eq. (134) into Eq. (133), we obtain that quantities ε, V and F' oscillate sinusoidally with the natural frequency

$$f_n = \frac{1}{2\pi} \sqrt{\frac{3 C \Phi_{1res} p^3 c_1 V_{1res} N_c'}{2 \pi J r_c'}} \qquad (135)$$

Obviously, quantity f_n is only one of the factors determining the time of transition of Φ_{1res} from one position to another.

A second important factor acting on response time is the magnitude of the damping torques, causing the quick decay of the oscillations.

According to the results of experiments made with the autodyne type AB, when changing over the voltage V_c from $+V_{cmax}$ to $-V_{cmax}$ a corresponding change of voltage V from $+V_{max}$ to $-V_{max}$ ensues within 0·2 sec. whereby the oscillations around $-V_{max}$ are quickly damped (see *Fig. 116*). A response time of this order of magnitude may be regarded as adequate in many fields of application, especially if it is considered that in many connections the response time is determined much less by the properties of the control type machine than by the inertia of all other elements connected with it.

Certainly, the AB type machine had a comparatively small rated power (a few kilowatts). Here the question arises, how the response speed of the autodyne changes with its dimensions.

Let us first investigate the effect of the dimensions of the machine upon the frequency of oscillations f_n. Since the peripheral speed of the armature is:

$$v_a = \frac{n}{60} \, \pi \, D_a = \frac{f}{p} \, \pi \, D_a \tag{136}$$

we assume that for maintaining

$$v_a = \text{constant} \tag{137}$$

the quantity p increases with D_a, that is

$$p \equiv D_a \tag{138}$$

In this case the pole pitch is

$$\tau = \frac{D_a \, \pi}{2 \, p} = \text{constant} \tag{139}$$

and the flux per pair of poles grows at a given flux density with armature length l_a, i. e.

$$\Phi_{1\text{res}} \equiv l_a \tag{140}$$

Further

$$n \equiv \frac{1}{p} \tag{141}$$

and

$$N_{\text{eff}} = \text{constant} \tag{142}$$

therefore

$$V_{1\text{res}} \cong E_{1\text{res}} \equiv \Phi_{1\text{res}} \equiv l_a \tag{143}$$

Finally

$$\frac{N_c'}{r_c'} \equiv \frac{q_c'}{l_{cm}'} \tag{144}$$

where q_c', is the cross section of one turn and l_{cm}' is the mean length of one turn of the control winding.

By taking into consideration that at $\tau = \text{constant}$ (see Eq. 139), the total cross section of winding $N_c' q_c'$ can increase only with the height of the pole core, which can be assumed as proportional to D_a, we obtain that at a given number of turns N_c'

$$q_c' \equiv D_a \tag{145}$$

Finally,

$$J \equiv D_a^4 l_a \tag{146}$$

In this way, by considering Eqs. (140), (138), (143), (144), (145) and (146), we obtain

$$f_n \equiv \sqrt{\frac{l_a^2 D_a^4}{D_a^2 l_a l'_{cm}}} = \sqrt{\frac{l_a}{l'_{cm}}} \tag{147}$$

The air gap of the machine being approximately proportional to D_a, it may be assumed that for maintaining the former flux densities, the mmf's F_{emax} and F'_{emax} of the exciting windings are to be chosen proportionally to D_a. On the other hand they are equal to

$$\frac{V_{max} N'_e}{r_e} \equiv \frac{V_{1res} q_e}{l_{em}} \tag{148}$$

where q_e and l_{em} are the cross section and mean length of the turns, respectively, of the exciting winding.

In this way we obtain

$$\frac{V_{1res} q_e}{l_{em}} \equiv D_a \tag{149}$$

and

$$\frac{q_e}{l_{em}} \equiv \frac{D_a}{V_{1res}} \equiv \frac{D_a}{l_a} \tag{150}$$

Therefore the damping mmf F'_{dmax} produced in this winding, when flux $\Phi_{1r\ s}$ is swinging with the frequency f_n, will be proportional to

$$F'_{dmax} \equiv \frac{\Phi_{1res} f_n q_e}{l_{em}} \equiv D_a \sqrt{\frac{l_a}{l'_{cm}}} \tag{151}$$

On the other hand, by considering Eqs. (143), (144) and (145), it follows from Eq. (125) that

$$F'_{max} \equiv \frac{V_{1res} q'_c}{l'_{cm}} \equiv \frac{l_a D_a}{l'_{cm}} \tag{152}$$

In commutator machines, when increasing the rated power and dimensions of the machine, the length of armature l_a is increased but slightly because of commutating problems; and l'_{cm} grows somewhat slower than l_a.

Then the following relation will be approximately valid

$$F'_{dmax} \equiv F'_{max} \tag{153}$$

Since similar considerations are valid for other stator windings as well, we may conclude from the above that the ratio of damping mmf to synchronizing mmf remains approximately constant in
the autodyne, when enlarging its rated power. On the other hand (if
l'_{cm} is taken proportional to l_a), f_n does not diminish by increasing the
dimensions. Therefore it may be assumed that *both of the principal
factors affecting the response speed of the autodyne remain unaltered,
i. e. the response speed practically does not decrease by increasing the
rated power. This result is the more interesting that in control type machines built on the basis of d-c generators, the response speed depends first
of all upon the relation of resistance to the inductance of the circuits, a
ratio which is known to decrease when increasing capacity.* It should be
noted that when deducing Eq. (140), we started from the supposition
that the flux density in the air gap does not increase by increasing the
dimensions. In reality, however, as is known, the flux density is
chosen higher in greater machines than in small ones, in consequence
of which $\Phi_{1\text{res}}$ and $V_{1\text{res}}$ grow rather than l_a.

On the other hand, when increasing the flux density, the
ratio of resistance to inductance diminishes even more.

In this way one comes to the conclusiont that starting from
certain rated powers the mentioned advantages of the autodyne are
supplemented by the circumstance of having a greater response speed
than the amplidyne.

Let us now turn back to autodynes with a response speed
of the above-mentioned order of magnitude, which is completely adequate for many purposes. Yet in certain fields of application such a
response speed is found too sluggish. An example is the d-c welding
requiring a very quick increase of voltage (within a small fraction of
a second) when passing from short circuit to no load, on the one hand,
and a limitation of current when passing suddenly from no load to
short circuit, on the other.

At the same time it is obvious that in the autodyne of *Fig. 18,*
if short-circuited, the current becomes very great in the first instant,
when the armature is not yet able to change its speed. This phenomenon, unimportant as it may be for the great majority of applications,
is not admissible in welding.

In order to match the properties of the autodyne also with
requirements of very quick response, we have developed its scheme
in this direction also. Though a thorough analysis of the principles

underlying such quick-response autodynes would exceed the limits of this book, we shall outline the main course leading to the solution of this problem.

Suppose the d-c winding of a $2p$ pole autodyne is construct-ed as a $4p$ pole winding *(Fig. 124)*. Then in the turns, in which emfs of the same direction are induced as in turns 3—3 and 4—4, obvi-

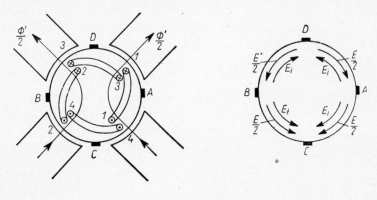

Fig. 124   Fig. 125

ously no emf will arise. In this relation the emfs $E/2$ generated by the direct-axis fluxes $\Phi'/2$ are distributed along the commutator circum-ference as shown in *Fig. 125*. The quadrature-axis fluxes $\Phi/2$ not shown in *Fig. 124*, induce similar emfs $E'/2$. Assume now that in the auto-dyne, beside the usual $2p$-pole fluxes Φ' and Φ, a $4p$-pole flux is present owing to some current i. Then the voltage induced by this current will be

$$E_i = c'i \qquad (154)$$

In this way between brushes A and D a voltage

$$\frac{E}{2} \pm c'i$$

may be obtained, where c' is a constant and the sign $\pm$ depends upon the direction of current i.

The phenomenon, however, should be pointed out that the mmf produced by the current of a $4p$-pole winding is not able to create compensating currents in a $2p$-pole phase winding to cancel the flux provoked by current i. Therefore at the appearance of current i

emf E_i is induced directly electromagnetically, contrary to voltage $E/2$ and $E'/2$ which can change only by the rotation of flux Φ_{1res}.

Assume, for instance, that for current i the load current I of a welding autodyne is chosen. In this case the voltage of the autodyne will be

$$V = E - c'I - \Sigma R\, I \tag{155}$$

where the part $I\,(c' + \Sigma R)$ arises practically with the appearance of I.

Suppose the machine operating at no load and $V = V_0 = V_{max} = E_{max}$. Evidently, even if E_{max} is supposed not to vary at all, the initial current, in case of a sudden short circuit, can reach only the transient short-circuit current

$$I_t = \frac{E_{max}}{c' + \Sigma R} \tag{156}$$

By the adequate choice of constant c' the value admissible for welding can readily be realized. After the appearance of current I_t, flux Φ_{1res} begins to rotate with respect to the stator. Consequently, E_{max} decreases to E_{min}, and I_t to the steady-state short-circuit current I_s corresponding to the control law of the autodyne. Here

$$E_{min} = I_s(c' + \Sigma R) \tag{157}$$

Similarly, when passing over from short circuit to no load with decreasing current I and a simultaneous decrement of $(c' + \Sigma R)\,I$, the voltage V increases very quickly to the transient no-load voltage V_{0t} yielding

$$V_{0t} = E_{min} - 0 = (c' + \Sigma R)\,I_s \tag{158}$$

even if initially neither Φ_{1res} changes its position nor E_{min} its value. Accordingly, E_{min} increases, owing to the spatial rotation of flux Φ_{1res}, until $V_0 = E_{max}$ is reached. In a similar way also other types of quick-response autodynes may be developed.

CHAPTER 22

COMMUTATION

A good commutation in the autodyne can be achieved in the steady state by means analogous to those used for the same purpose in ordinary converters. Since current I_1 is a compensating current set up by the mmf F_I of the load current I, the influence of the resulting

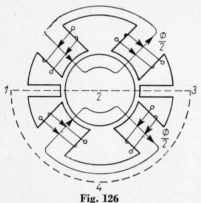

mmf produced by these two currents will be but very little. The reactance voltage e_r produced by current I is partly compensated by the reactance voltage induced by current I_1. The resulting reactance voltage and the effect of the remaining non-compensated part of the armature mmf on the commutating zone, can be eliminated by the aid of a commutating-pole winding carrying current I.

Fig. 126

The influence of oscillations of the mmf produced by current I_1 on commutation, amounting to about ± 7 per cent and having the frequency $2mf$ (where m is the number of phases), can easily be diminished to a harmless value by enlarging the air gap under the commutating poles.

Let us investigate now the effect of the quadrature-axis flux Φ on commutation in the autodyne with uniformly arranged half poles *(Fig. 59)*.

As the exciting windings do not comprise the commutating zone, but only the respective half poles, flux Φ passes in form of two equal branches *(Fig. 126)* along the commutating zone and the commutating poles. Thereby the sum of mmf's produced, within the path $1-2-3-4-1$, by the system of stator excitation windings, is zero.

On the other hand, this system, as is known, eliminates current I_{mres} from the armature. Consequently, not even a part of the flux passes through the air gap under the commutating poles.

The same applies to the autodynes with unequally distributed half poles *(Fig. 58b)*, when the quadrature-axis winding consists of coils arranged on the corresponding half poles. In an autodyne with the configuration shown in *Fig. 58a,* the quadrature-axis winding is produced like the pole-face-neutralizing winding of a d-c machine, consequently, the quadrature-axis mmf comprises the commutating poles. But in this case also, it can be achieved easily that the algebraic sum of the exciting mmf's within the said closed path be zero. It is sufficient to produce an mmf proportionate and opposite to current I_e on the commutating poles.

Let us examine now how the dynamic commutation in the autodynes is performed. In order to understand why this problem is entirely solved in the autodyne, while in a converter it causes great difficulties, we shall briefly examine of what the problem consists.

As is known, certain difficulties in commutation arise in the rotary converter at sudden changes of load, because the change in current I_1 and the corresponding mmf F_1 is lagging behind the change in current I and mmf F_I *(Fig. 127)*. If, for instance, F_I grows according to law $F_I = f(t)$, then $F_1 \cong \lambda f(t)$, where $\lambda < 1$. Consequently, residual mmf's of the value $(1 - \lambda) f(t)$ arise, and the corresponding flux induces high voltages in the short-circuited windings and sets up considerable additional torque, causing the swinging of the armature.

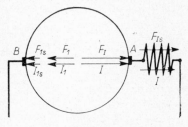

Fig. 127

The reason why this phenomenon arises, can readily be understood from the explanations concerning the converter in *Chapters 3* and *13*.

In *Chapter 13* it has been explained precisely that the load current provokes a definite braking torque, which is added to the torque of friction. Hence the angle γ represented in *Fig. 7* increases further. In the steady state, evidently different angles γ correspond to different load currents I. If, however, at a sudden change in load, current I grows quickly, then angle γ is no longer in accordance with the increased braking torque. Consequently, the rotor decelerates and vector $\overline{V_{1res}}$ rotates anticlockwise, whereby angle γ between $\overline{E_{1res}}$ and $-\overline{V_{1res}}$ becomes greater. After reaching the angle complying with the new value of I, the armature, owing to its inertia, is unable to accelerate instantaneously to synchronism, which has the consequence that vector $\overline{V_{1res}}$ continues to rotate anticlockwise and a residual accelerating torque is produced. Thus, oscillations of the armature are provoked on the one hand, and a corresponding difference of mmf, on the other, produced by currents I and I_1, changing their direction periodically.

In the autodyne this phenomenon is entirely eliminated. If we succeed in building up in the rotor, beside current I_1, a supplementary alternating current I_{1s} coinciding in direction with the former and producing an mmf varying according to the law $F_{1s} = (1 - \lambda) f(t)$, then the above-mentioned residual mmf's with all their harmful consequences will disappear.

Since, according to the theory of compensating currents, any alternating current can be generated by mmf's of opposite direction, the mmf F_{1s} changing in function of time can be produced by a stator mmf varying in function of time, if

$$F_{Is} = (1 - \lambda) f(t) = (1 - \lambda) F_I \equiv I$$

This requires the creation of an mmf F_{Is} produced in the direction shown in *Fig. 127* by load current I.

It follows therefrom that the phenomenon described above cannot arise in an autodyne in which, according to its fundamental principle, all internal torques provoked by current I are eliminated.

As shown in *Chapter 13*, the quadrature-axis series coil according to *Fig. 78a*, eliminates the torques due to higher harmonics, by changing somewhat current I_1. It follows that this winding, which at any change in current I forces the changes in current I_1 and is therefore termed in this respect forcing winding, beside increasing the control accuracy, performs also the task of completely eliminating the enumerated phenomena arising at sudden changes of load in converters.

By means of the above measures an entirely sparkless commutation was achieved in the autodynes according to *Figs. 16* or *23*.

At sudden changes in load neither swings, nor oscillations, nor commutation disturbances related to them, were observed.

The oscillogram in *Fig. 128*, recorded on an $AZ-250/36$ type autodyne with an initial voltage $V = 36$ V and at a sudden change in load resistance, shows that by using a forcing winding the possibility of armature oscillations is eliminated. As is to be seen, the operation of the autodyne was completely stable and practically without any oscillation of the output voltage V, i. e. without any mechanical swing of the armature.

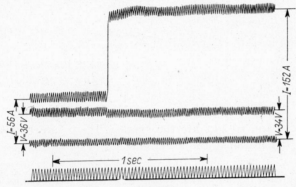

Fig. 128

The commutation of the experimental autodynes conformed at rated load to degree $1 \div 1\ ^1/_2$, where degree 1 represents the optimum commutation without any sparking.

The continuous operation of the machine at rated load was not detrimental to commutation, either in case of great changes in load or, in the autodyne of *Fig. 16*, at sudden short circuits accompanied by corresponding changes in angle β. The commutation of the autodyne of series AZ was, at an intense load current (150—250 A), entirely sparkless (degree 1). The commutation remained satisfactory also in case of transient phenomena occurring, when switching the load current on and off.

When starting the autodyne $AZ-140/72$, a certain amount of sparking occurs which, however, ceases when the rotor pulls into synchronism. This might be attributed to the wave winding, in whose turns, short-circuited through the brushes, an important transformatory emf is induced. Evidently, in designing high-capacity autodynes, it will be expedient to recur to some well-known measure for maximally diminishing the transformatory emf (e. g. by lap winding).

EFFICIENCY, WEIGHT AND SIZE OF AUTODYNES

The investigation of different kinds of losses in the autodyne and their influence on design would exceed the limits of this book. It should, however, be emphasized that the autodyne, like the rotary converter, has, on the one hand, smaller dimensions and weight and, on the other, smaller losses than a motor generator and while space requirements and weight are the smaller, the greater the admissible losses are. For instance, the autodyne AZ—140/72 built according to *Fig. 16* for a rated power of 10 kW, has a size 40 per cent less, an efficiency 3 per cent higher and a weight 25 per cent lower than the motor generator AZD of the same capacity, used for the same purpose, although this latter has no automatic control. Moreover, the autodyne has proved to have a reserve capacity of 15 per cent. It should be added that the autodyne mentioned above has separate d-c and a-c windings, which is known from the theory of converters to involve a low rate of utilization of the armature. In this case, space requirements, weight and losses were decreased by having only two coil ends in the armature instead of four, and only two bearings instead of four, as well as by omitting the clutch.

If the armature is constructed, as is usual for rotary converters with the normal ratio V_{max}/V_{1rcs}, with a winding carrying in most cases only the difference of the alternating current and the direct current, then space requirements, weight and losses of the autodyne can be further diminished.

When comparing the control winding of the autodyne and of a corresponding motor generator, it should be remembered that they invest the autodyne with properties a d-c generator may acquire only by the aid of the same windings and by adding a separate auxiliary control type machine.

Moreover, as to space requirements, the fact that the autodyne has several stator windings, is greatly compensated by the fact that the exciting mmf in the autodyne is much smaller than in a d-c generator, because the air gap under the poles can be made much smaller. This is due to the practically complete elimination of the armature reaction in the autodyne and the fact that the thickness of the air gap does not affect the synchronizing torques (see *Chapter 6*).

In case of repeated sudden change in load, the space requirements, weight and losses of the autodyne can be diminished also because the conversion from a-c to d-c power is achieved in a direct electromagnetic way and not by converting electrical power into mechanical power and vice versa. This effects not only the shaft diameter but also the size of the asynchronous motor, which should have a great reserve to be prevented from pulling out, or at least to avoid the considerable speed drop and generator voltage dip. All these circumstances are absent in the autodyne.

In comparing the autodyne with a motor generator concerning weight, space requirements and losses, it should be taken into consideration that the autodyne operates at the same time, without enlarged dimensions, as a synchronous condenser (see *Chapter 24)* and furnishes reactive power to the mains.

These questions were investigated on the experimental autodyne A—3B and on the autodyne AZ — 140/72. The efficiency was measured by the ratio of wattmetre readings on the d-c and a-c side. The efficiency of the autodyne A — 3B amounted to 73·7 per cent; it should be remarked in addition that in the circuit of the exciting windings and in that of the friction-compensating windings, regulating resistances absent in normal operation were inserted, increasing thereby the power loss.

By considering that in serial production these resistances are absent and therefore their losses are to be excluded from the power balance, the efficiency of the machine A—3B with series-connected control winding is obtained to be 77·7 per cent. The efficiency of the autodyne AZ — 140/72, measured at a 10 kW output power, with the connection of *Fig. 16* was 74 per cent and with the connection of *Fig. 23* it was 77 per cent.

Tables 3 and *4* show the efficiency, weight and space requirements of realized autodynes compared with the corresponding values for motor generators having the same capacity, voltage and speed.

TABLE 3

Types	Rated output power, kW	Rated voltage, V	Rated input power, kW	Efficiency, per cent	Max, length, width, height, mm	Volume according to main dimensions, dm³	Specific volume, dm³/kW	Weight, kg	Specific weight, kg/kW
Autodynes A—3B A—6B	3·57	230	4·5	77·7	690 × × 385× × 396	105	29·5	130	35·5
Motor generator consisting of a generator PH—28·5 and of an asynchronous motor AD—32/2	3·4	215	4·95	83× 85 = = 70·5	900 × × 366·5 × 376	124	36·5	142	42·0

TABLE 4

Types	Rated output power, kW	Rpm	Efficiency, per cent	Max, length, width, height, mm	Volume according to main dimensions, dm³	Specific volume, dm³/kW	Weight, kg	Specific weight, kg/kW
Autodyne AZ — 140/72	10	1500	74	950× × 615× × 625	365	36·5	435	43·5
Motor generator AZD—7·5/60	7·5	1450	64·5	1370× × 550× × 660				
Motor generator AZD—12/60	12	1450	68	1389× × 550× × 660				
Motor generator obtained by interpolation between machines AZD — 7·5/60 and AZD — 12/60	10	1450	66·25	1379× × 550× × 660	500	50	585	58·5

The autodynes A—3B and A—6B are compared with a motor generator, consisting of a d-c generator, type PH—28.5, and of a three-phase asynchronous motor, type AD—32/2. The autodyne AZ—140/72 has been compared with the motor generator type AZD. The data of this machine for 10 kW rated power are obtained by interpolation between the technical data of the machine AZD—7.5/60 and AZD—12/60.

These tables substantiate the theoretical statements made above, according to which the autodynes have smaller size, weight and losses than the corresponding motor generators.

The autodynes A—3B and A—6B, for instance, have a volume 1·18 time smaller and a weight 1·08 time lower than the motor generator set composed of machines PH—28·5 and AD—32/2. The autodyne AZ—140/72 has a volume 1·37 time smaller and a weight 1·34 time lower than the motor generator AZD having the same rated power. Nevertheless, it should be considered that — as shown by the tests carried out on the machine AZ—140/72 — this is not sufficiently utilized as far as heating is concerned and has therefore a 15 per cent reserve in capacity.

Let it be remembered that the main parameters of the AZ type autodyne are given in *Fig. 37*.

The losses in the autodynes A—3B, A—6B with a rated power of 3·5 kW are by 470 W less than in the motor generator set consisting of a PH—28·5 and an AD 32/2 type machine and having the same rated power. In the autodyne AZ—140/72, at a rated power of 10 kW, the losses are by 1650 W less than in a motor generator AZD computed for the same rated power.

It should be noted that the losses, main dimensions and weight of the experimental autodynes and of the AZ type autodynes are not characteristic of the economic properties of autodynes, because the machines A—3B and A—6B and the AZ type autodynes, complying with technical requirements, were designed according to an economically unfavourable ratio of a-c voltage V_{1res} to the maximum d-c voltage V_{max}.

The ratio of voltages determined by technical conditions in the AZ type autodyne $V_{1res}/V_{max} = 5·3$ required those machines to be realized with two entirely separated windings in the armature, involving an increase in losses and main dimensions, and also in costs. The machines A—3B and A—6B were also constructed with a supplementary a-c winding, connected to the d-c winding like the winding of an an autotransformer.

As the theory of the autodyne shows, in case of $V_{1r\,s}/V_{max} = = 0\cdot55—0\cdot6$ the machine can be built with a unique winding in the armature, diminishing greatly the losses, dimensions and the corresponding production expenses and operational costs. The more the ratio $V_{1r\,s}/V_{max}$ approaches the value $0\cdot55—0\cdot6$, the more effectively the machine is utilized.

Obviously, better results as to efficiency, dimensions, weight and costs are obtained with autodynes used for such purposes as, for instance, electrical drives, when a more favourable ratio of $V_{1r\,s}/V_{max}$ is possible, than for autodynes of series AZ.

It should be added that the motor generators compared with the autodynes consist of machines, built on the basis of long years, experience concerning design and technology, which can hardly be said for autodynes.

These circumstances partly account for the somewhat higher costs and work requirements of autodynes (by some 30 per cent higher than for motor generators of the AZD type of the same rated power).

It may, for instance, be pointed out that the machine AZ has been constructed for 1500 rpm, while it could have been built easily for 3000 rpm. Nevertheless, the diminution of dimensions, and weight could be attained with motor generators of the type AZD as well, if they were built for the same higher rpm. Yet, an additional condition would arise in the autodyne, strongly diminishing the production time, costs and dimensions in comparison to the AZD type motor generators. This means that when increasing the synchronous speed of the AZ type autodyne, the number of half poles would decrease from 8 to 4, i. e. to the number of poles of the AZD type motor generators. By taking into consideration that the work required of the AZ type machine depends, first of all, on the construction of the half poles and their windings, it will be clear that a decrease of the number of poles by half would considerably diminish the costs of the machine.

CHAPTER 24

SAVINGS IN ELECTRIC ENERGY WITH THE
AUTODYNE BY SUPPLYING REACTIVE POWER
TO THE MAINS

In the armature of an autodyne with stator slip excitation at no load, practically no alternating current is flowing. When loaded, direct current I produces in the rotor the mmf F_I *(Fig. 129)*, provoking a compensating alternating current $\overline{I_1}$. The component $\overline{I_1} \cos \varphi$

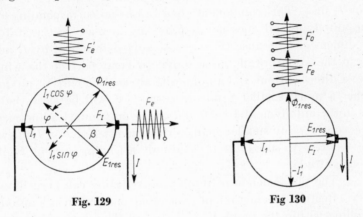

Fig. 129   Fig 130

is the active current, while component $\overline{I_1} \sin \varphi$ is a leading reactive current. Thus, when the active load diminishes because of decreasing V at constant current I, the behaviour of the machine automatically approaches more and more the performance of a synchronous condenser, and the autodyne improves the power factor of the network.

Here it should be emphasized that this phenomenon has nothing common with that known from the theory of ordinary converter, consisting in obtaining the leading current by increasing the mmf of the stator excitation *(Fig. 130)*. In this machine the current I_1, necessary for compensating the mmf F_I of current I, is an active current, since $\beta \simeq 0$. It follows that, when the mmf F'_e is big enough to establish a flux inducing the emf E_{1res}, the reactive current will be zero. It may, however, be obtained in form of current $-I_1'$ by adding to F_e' the mmf of "overexcitation" F_o', compensated by the mmf of current $-I_1'$.

The creation of mmf F_o' causes additive losses and necessitates a corresponding increase of the stator dimensions. At the same time, the leading current I_1' causes supplementary losses in the armature, requiring an enlargement of the rotor dimensions.

The conditions creating a leading current in the autodyne are, however, quite different in principle. Here a phenomenon arises that could be called "rotor overexcitation" in contrary to the "stator overexcitation". As seen from *Fig. 129*, the fundamental of the d-c rotor mmf F_I has a component coinciding with Φ_{1res}. Since the flux is already ensured by the mmf's of windings N_e', and N_e, this component builds up a compensating current in the form of a leading a-c component $I_1 \sin \varphi$. This component then causes no corresponding losses in the autodyne and does not require any increase in the stator or rotor dimensions, because these are already determined by I_1 and I. Since in the armature of the autodyne a great part of the winding carries a direct current and an opposite alternating current producing together a much smaller resulting current, it will be clear that the losses in the autodyne at $V = 0$ and at the maximum leading current, will be considerably smaller than in the converter of *Fig. 130*, even if the latter were to supply at no load only a leading current I_1' of the same magnitude.

The phenomenon of rotor overexcitation can be utilized for a very effective production of a leading current in all autodynes controlling within the limits $V_{max} > V > 0$. The diminution of losses with respect to the converter and also the supply of the leading reactive current and power by the autodyne ensure considerable savings in electric energy.

If the AZD type motor generator of 10 kW capacity is replaced by an AZ—140/72 type autodyne, the losses will be smaller by $\Delta P_P = 1 \cdot 65$ kW owing to better efficiency.

At the same time, thanks to the leading current supplied by the autodyne, a gain in reactive power $\Delta Q = 7 \text{ kVAr} + 8 \cdot 35 \text{ kVAr} = 15 \cdot 35 \text{ kVAr}$ is achieved, as it may be seen from *Table 5*.

If the coefficient of economic equivalence of the reactive power at the consumers $K_{ee} = 0 \cdot 15$ kW/kVAr is taken into consideration (determining the losses caused by the generation and transmission of reactive power), the gain in reactive power will be found to correspond to a supplementary saving in active power

$$\Delta P_Q = K_{ee} \, \Delta Q = 0.15 \cdot 15.35 \, \text{kW} = 2.3 \, \text{kW}$$

TABLE 5

Type	Power, kW	Power factor	Reactive power, kVAr
Supposed motor generator AZD	10	0.873 lagging	8.35 ind.
Autodyne AZ—140/72	10	0.9 leading	7 cap.

The total gain in active power when using an AZ—140/72 type autodyne in place of an AZD type motor generator will be:

$$\Sigma \, \Delta P = \Delta P_P + \Delta P_Q = 1.65 \, \text{kW} + 2.3 \, \text{kW} = 3.95 \, \text{kW}$$

Hence, if the autodyne operates eight hours a day, i. e. $T = 2400$ hours a year, the saving in electric energy in a year will be

$$\Sigma \, \Delta P \cdot T = 3.95 \, \text{kW} \cdot 2400 \, \text{h} = 9500 \, \text{kWh}$$

The cost of this electric energy, according to the mean industrial tariff valid in the energetical system "Mosenergo", i. e. 14.5 kopeks per kWh, will amount to 1380 roubles, i. e. the machine at a price of 7000 roubles (in 1952) will be settled within five years.

If the autodyne is supposed to operate in three shifts, i. e. $T = 7200$ hours a year, then by assuming ten per cent repair and maintenance, we obtain the gain in electric energy per annum as

$$\Sigma \, \Delta P \cdot 0.9 \cdot T = 3.95 \, \text{kW} \cdot 0.9 \cdot 7200 \, \text{h} = 25 \, 500 \, \text{kWh}$$

This energy will cost 3700 roubles.

In this case the AZ—140/72 type autodyne will pay within the first two years of its use, on the basis of electric energy saved.

Here too, the gain should be added, which is obtained by the higher rate of utilization of the transformers and the electrical power system achieved by freeing them from reactive power.

In order to obtain, for a motor generator set driven by an asynchronous motor, an additional reactive power of 15 kVAr with leading power factor, one would need, beside a 10 kW generator and a 13 kW motor, a special phase compensator, i. e. a static or synchronous condenser of 15 kVAr. But then part of the active power gain achieved by the latter would be lost owing to the internal losses arising in it, while the supply of leading current from the autodyne does not involve any increase of losses.

This property is one of the chief advantages of autodynes over devices, in which rectifiers are used, for a stepless control of d-c voltage (e. g. with dry-plate type or semiconductor rectifiers controlled by reactors or grid-controlled mercury arc rectifiers) and which — as it is well-known — have in average a low power factor.

SUMMARY

1. The autodyne is a new electric machine substituting a motor generator set consisting of an a-c motor and a d-c generator by a single machine of essentially smaller dimensions. It represents at the same time a special control type machine and a phase compensator. Consequently, it replaces simultaneously four machines altogether.

2. The autodyne is apt to maintain automatically any quantity Π_1 expressed electrically at a desired reference input Π_2 either constant or varying, according to whatever law.

3. The controllable quantity Π_1 may be represented by the voltage or the current of the autodyne, or by an arbitrary quantity arising in another circuit (e. g. in the load circuit, in the exciting or control circuit).

4. The autodyne stabilizes the controllable quantity Π_1 according to a definite reference value Π_2 with a great degree of accuracy.

5. The process of maintaining certain quantities constant and the automatic self-control of the autodyne is stable.

6. The autodyne operates with high stability also at any sudden change in mains voltage or in load current.

7. The commutation of the autodyne is favourable both in the steady state and in case of transients.

8. The autodyne can work also as an inverter converting d-c power into a-c power (e. g. formation of batteries, regenerative braking of driving motors).

9. The autodyne has essentially smaller power losses and a higher efficiency than the corresponding motor generator sets.

10. In consequence of rotor overexcitation, the autodyne supplies great leading currents and reactive power to the mains without having to increase the dimensions or power losses.

11. The results achieved in the production of autodynes justify the hope that this new electric machine will essentially extend the possibilities of automation and will be used in many fields of electrical engineering.

LIST OF SYMBOLS

a, a'	constants
A_1, A_2, A_3, A_4	constants
b	constant
β	angle between vectors $\Phi_{1\text{res}}$ and Φ'
$\Delta\beta$	small change in angle β
$c_1 \ldots c_{15}$	constants
$c_1' \ldots c_4', c_8', c_9', c'$	constants
$C_1, C_1' \ldots C_4'$	constants
C_R, C_H	constants
D_a	diameter of the armature
e_r	reactance emf induced at commutation
$E_\sim$	induced a-c emf occurring in case of slip between the main brushes in the quadrature axis
E	induced d-c emf between the main brushes in the quadrature axis
ΔE	small change in voltage E
E'	induced d-c emf between the auxiliary brushes in the direct axis
E_1	fundamental of induced phase emf in the quadrature axis
E_1'	fundamental of induced phase emf in the direct axis
$\overline{E_{1\text{res}}}$	resultant of vectors $\overline{E_1}$ and $\overline{E_1'}$
$E_{1\text{res}}$	magnitude of emf vector $\overline{E_{1\text{res}}}$
E_f	component of induced phase emf in the rotary converter due to friction torque
E_i	additional emf induced electromagnetically
E_A	internal emf of an accumulator battery
ε	angle
f	mains frequency
f_n	natural frequency of oscillations in the autodyne

$\Delta F'$	small control mmf acting in the direct axis	
F'_c	mmf due to control current i_c	
F_e	mmf in the quadrature-axis exciting winding	
F'_e	mmf in the direct-axis exciting winding	
F_f	mmf in the quadrature-axis friction-compensating winding	
F'_f	mmf in the direct-axis friction-compensating winding	
F'_o	mmf corresponding to stator overexcitation	
F_r	residual mmf due to incomplete compensation of internal friction torques	
F_I	mmf due to d-c current I	
F_1	mmf due to a-c current I_1	
F_{1s}	mmf due to current I_{1s}	(expressed in ampere-turns)
F_{ls}	mmf in the stator for compensating F_{1s}	
F_R	mmf due to the rotor current	
F_S	mmf due to the stator current	
F_Φ	difference of F_R and F_S	

Φ	total quadrature-axis flux
Φ'	total direct-axis flux
$\overline{\Phi_{1\mathrm{res}}}$	spatial fundamental vector of the main flux
$\Phi_{1\mathrm{res}}$	magnitude of the fundamental flux vector
$\overline{\Phi_1}$	quadrature-axis component of $\overline{\Phi_{1\mathrm{res}}}$
$\overline{\Phi'_1}$	direct-axis component of $\overline{\Phi_{1\mathrm{res}}}$
Φ_q	small quadrature-axis flux due to harmonics
Φ_{qC}	quadrature-axis flux compensating Φ_q
γ	angle
$\Delta\gamma$	small change in angle γ
i_c	control current
	load current on the d-c side
ΔI	small change in load current I
I_1	phase current component compensating I
I_1	phase current component perpendicular to I_1
$\Delta I_1, \Delta I'_1$	small change in currents I_1 and I'_1, respectively
I_{1C}	compensating phase current in the armature
I_{1s}	supplementary alternating current
$\Delta I'_d$	direct-axis phase current compensating the effects of stator damping currents
I_e	exciting current in the quadrature-axis winding for stator slip excitation

I'_e	exciting current in the direct-axis winding for stator slip excitation;
I_f	armature current component in the converter due to friction torque
$\overline{I_m}$	quadrature-axis component of the magnetizing current in the armature
$\overline{I'_m}$	direct-axis component of the magnetizing current in the armature
$\overline{I_{mres}}$	resultant of vectors $\overline{I'_m}$ and $\overline{I_m}$
I_{mres}	magnitude of $\overline{I_{mres}}$
ΔI_s	synchronizing three-phase current in the converter
I_s	steady-state short-circuit current
I_t	transient short-circuit current
I_A	current of an accumulator
I_C	compensating current
I_D	current of a d-c source
J	moment of inertia
$k_1,\ k_2$	constants
$K_1,\ K_2,\ K_3$	constants
K_{ee}	coefficient of economic equivalence of reactive power
l_a	effective length of the armature
l_{em}	mean length of the turns of the exciting winding
l'_{cm}	mean length of the turns of the control winding
λ	ratio figure
m	number of phases
n	number of revolutions (rotational speed)
Δn	small change in n
n_s	synchronous speed
N and N'	quadrature-axis and direct-axis control windings, resp.
N_c and N'_c	quadrature-axis and direct-axis control windings, resp.
N_e and N'_e	quadrature-axis and direct-axis excitation windings, resp.
N_f and N'_f	quadrature-axis and direct-axis windings for compensation of friction torque, resp.
N_F	forcing winding
$N_{.ff}$	effective number of turns (of the armature)
$N_{R\approx}$	number of turns of the phase winding on the rotor
$N_{R=}$	number of turns of the d-c winding on the rotor
ω	angular speed

or the corresponding number of turns

p	number of pairs of poles
P	power
P_{mres}	active power of current I_{mres}
ΔP_s	synchronizing power
ΔP_P	loss (in active power)
ΔP_Q	power gain equivalent to the reactive power
$\Sigma \Delta P$	entire gain of active power, due to amelioration of efficiency and feeding reactive power into the network
Π_1, Π_2	quantities to be compared
ΔQ	gain in reactive power
q_e	cross section of the exciting winding
q_c'	cross section of the control winding
r, r_1	resistances
r_c'	resistance of the control winding
r_B	brush resistances
r_C	resistance of the commutating pole winding
r_F	resistance of the forcing winding
r_N	resistance of winding N
$r_{N'}$	resistance of winding N'
R	resistances
R_L	load resistance
ΣR_a	resultant internal resistance of the main circuit of the autodyne
T	electrodynamic torque
ΔT	small change in torque T
ΔT_a	small accelerating torque
ΔT_b	small braking torque
ΔT_{d_1}	small damping torque due to direct-axis damping currents
ΔT_{d_2}	small damping torque due to quadrature-axis damping currents
ΔT_d	sum of ΔT_{d_1} and ΔT_{d_2}
ΔT_{dd}	damping torque resulting as a consequence of diminishing factors
T_f	friction torque
T_r	reluctance torque
v_a	peripheral spead of the armature
$V_\sim$	alternating voltage occurring in case of slip between the main brushes in the quadrature axis
V	d-c voltage between the quadrature-axis brushes
V'	d-c voltage between the direct-axis brushes
ΔV	small change in V
$\Delta V'$	small change in V'

$\overline{V_{1\text{re}}}$	three-phase terminal voltage vector
$V_{1\text{res}}$	magnitude of $\overline{V_{1\text{res}}}$
$\overline{V_1}$	quadrature-axis component of the terminal voltage
$\overline{V_1'}$	direct-axis component of the terminal voltage
$\Delta V_1', \Delta V_1$	small changes in V_1' and V
V_a	voltage of the autodyne
V_c	control voltage
ΔV_c	small change in V_c
V_C, V_{C_1}, V_{C_2}	constant voltages
V_A	voltage of an accumulator battery
V_D	voltage of a d-c source
V_G	voltage of a generator
V_L	voltage of the load
V_0	d-c no-load voltage
V_{ot}	transient no-load voltage

Responsible for publication

GY. BERNÁT

Director of the Publishing House of the Hungarian Academy of Sciences

✳

Responsible editor

G. DIENES

✳

Technical editor

I. HÚTH

✳

Manuscript received: January, 1960, printed in 2500 copies, 17,15 (A/5) sheets
Made in Hungary at the Academy Press, Budapest no 50586
Responsible manager: GY. BERNÁT